Collins Spanish Club

FUN, ACTIVE LEARNING

Book 2

Ruth Sharp & Rosi McNab

First published in 2009 by Collins
an imprint of HarperCollins Publishers
77-85 Fulham Palace Road
London W6 8JB

www.collinslanguage.com

9 8 7 6 5 4 3 2 1 0

A catalogue record for this book is available from the British Library

Authors: Ruth Sharp and Rosi McNab
Illustrator: Mel Sharp
Designers: Rob Payne and Richard Marston

ISBN: 978-0-00-784005-2

This edition produced for The Book People Ltd,
Park Menai, Bangor LL57 4FB

CD recording by Talking Issues
Actors: Elena Pavan Macías, Victoria Galache-Brown,
Alex Winslow Parsons and Ainara Campo
Printed in China through
Golden Cup Printing Services

Contents

1. Me and my friends

Yo

Me

Track 1

Key words
yo I
(yo) soy I am
(yo) tengo I have
mi(s) my

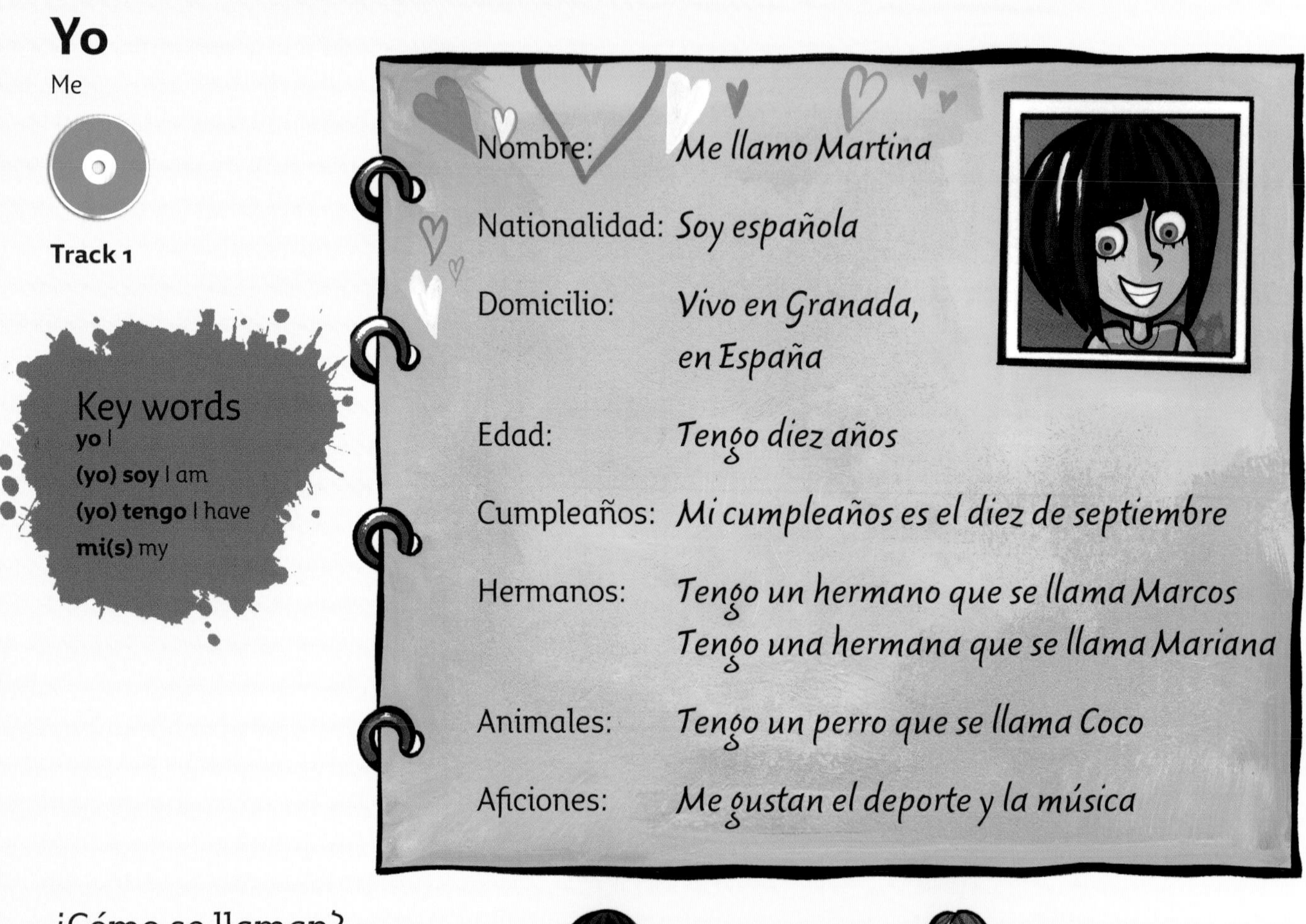

¿Cómo se llaman?

What are they called?

1. ....
2. ....
3. ....
4. ....

¡El detective!

Did you notice?

In Spanish, you say 'I **have** 10 years' instead of 'I **am** 10 years old'

Completa la página sobre ti y pega una foto tuya en el espacio

Complete the page for yourself and stick a photo of yourself in the space

Truco

Remember to use *el* or *la* in the last sentence. Also, add *-n* to *gusta* if you want to write two things you like: *Me gusta**n** **el** tenis y **la** lectura.*

Mini Diccionario

¿Cuándo es tu compleaños?
When is your birthday?
Los meses del año
The months of the year
enero febrero marzo abril mayo junio julio agosto septiembre octubre noviembre diciembre

Nombre: Me llamo
....

Nacionalidad: Soy ....

Domicilio: Vivo en ...., en ....

Edad: Tengo .... años

Cumpleaños: Mi cumpleaños es el ....
....

Hermanos: Tengo ....
....

Animales: Tengo ....

Aficiones: Me gusta ....

Hermanos Brothers and sisters

Tengo un hermano/dos hermanos I have one brother/two brothers

Tengo una hermana/dos hermanas I have one sister/two sisters

No tengo hermanos I don't have any brothers or sisters

No tengo animales I don't have any pets

The word *hermanos* can mean 'brothers' or it can be used to refer to 'brothers *and* sisters', like the word 'siblings' in English. You use *hermanas* when only referring to sisters.

¿Qué país? Which country?

Vivo en Inglaterra/Escocia/Gales/Irlanda (del Norte)
I live in England/Scotland/Wales/(Northern) Ireland

¿Qué nacionalidad? Saying what nationality you are:

Soy... inglés/inglesa	**escocés/escocesa**	**galés/galesa**	**irlandés/irlandesa**
I'm... English	Scottish	Welsh	Irish

Aficiones Hobbies

Me gusta(n)... I like...		*masculine*	*feminine*
	singular	**el deporte**	**la música**
		el cine	**la tele**
	plural	**los animales**	**las películas**

Me gusta la escuela I like school

¡Me encantan las vacaciones! I love the holidays!

Truco

The nationalities with *-a* on the end are the feminine forms. There is a more detailed list of nationalities on page 60.

Mi mejor amigo

My best friend [male]

Escucha el CD y completa la página sobre Lucas

Listen to the CD and complete the page for Lucas

Key words

él he
(él) es he is
(él) tiene he has
su, sus his

Track 2

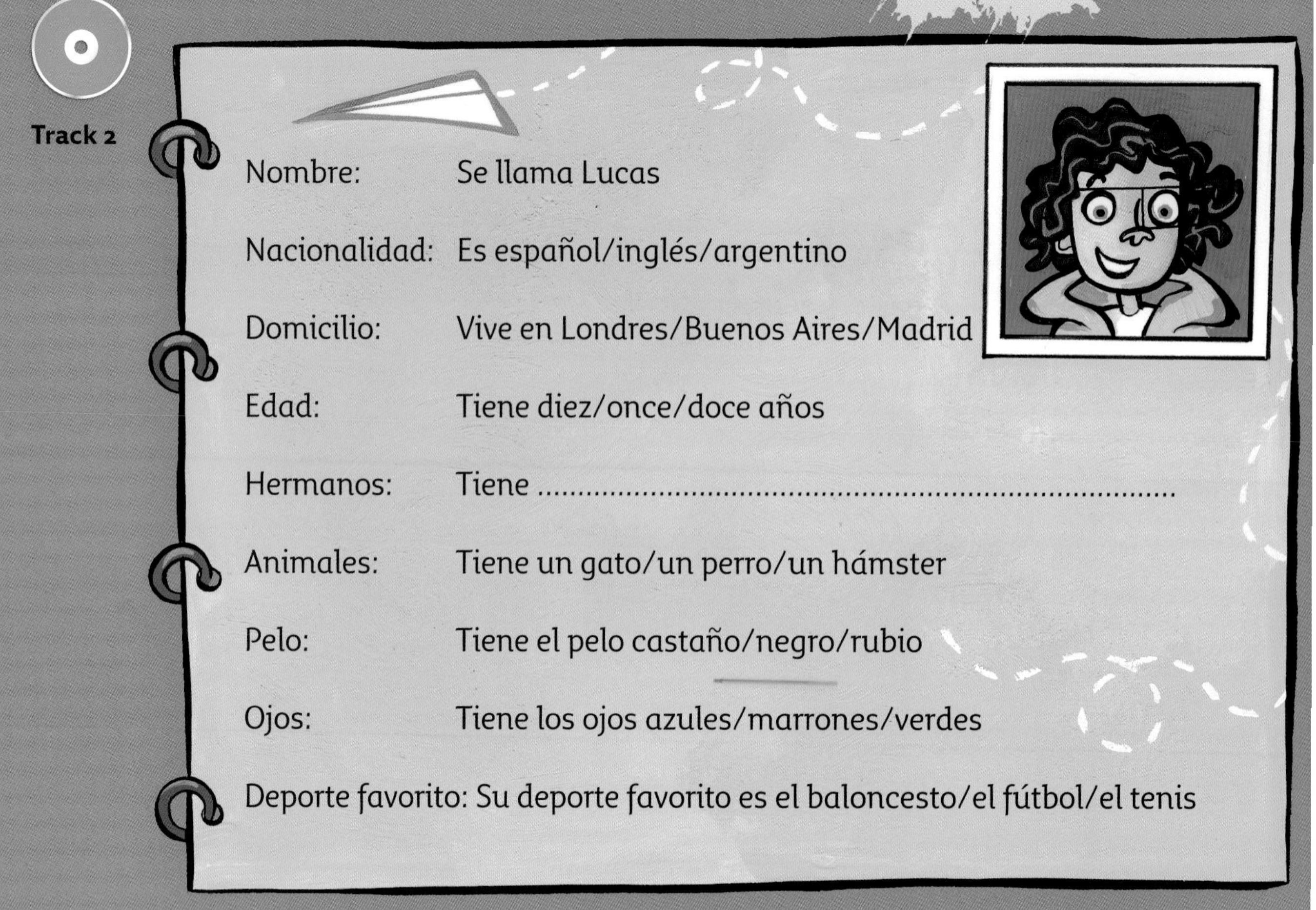

Nombre: Se llama Lucas

Nacionalidad: Es español/inglés/argentino

Domicilio: Vive en Londres/Buenos Aires/Madrid

Edad: Tiene diez/once/doce años

Hermanos: Tiene ....

Animales: Tiene un gato/un perro/un hámster

Pelo: Tiene el pelo castaño/negro/rubio

Ojos: Tiene los ojos azules/marrones/verdes

Deporte favorito: Su deporte favorito es el baloncesto/el fútbol/el tenis

¿Lo sabías?

Lucas is from Argentina in South America. Spanish is spoken in most South and Central American countries but the accent sounds quite different from the one you hear in Spain. In South America, they pronounce *c* as *s* (rather than *th*) and in Argentina, *ll* is pronounced like the English *sh*. People often say the Argentinians sound like they are singing when they speak.

¿Qué animal es?

Which animal is it?

un perro

un gato

un hámster

un pececito rojo

una cobaya

un conejo

Truco

Do the ones you know first and see what you have left. Can you guess them or do you need to look them up? If you need a dictionary, go online to www.collinslanguage.com.

Mi mejor amiga

My best friend [female]

Mira las imágenes y completa la página sobre Isabel

Look at the pictures and complete the page for Isabel

Key words

ella she

(ella) es she is

(ella) tiene she has

su, sus her

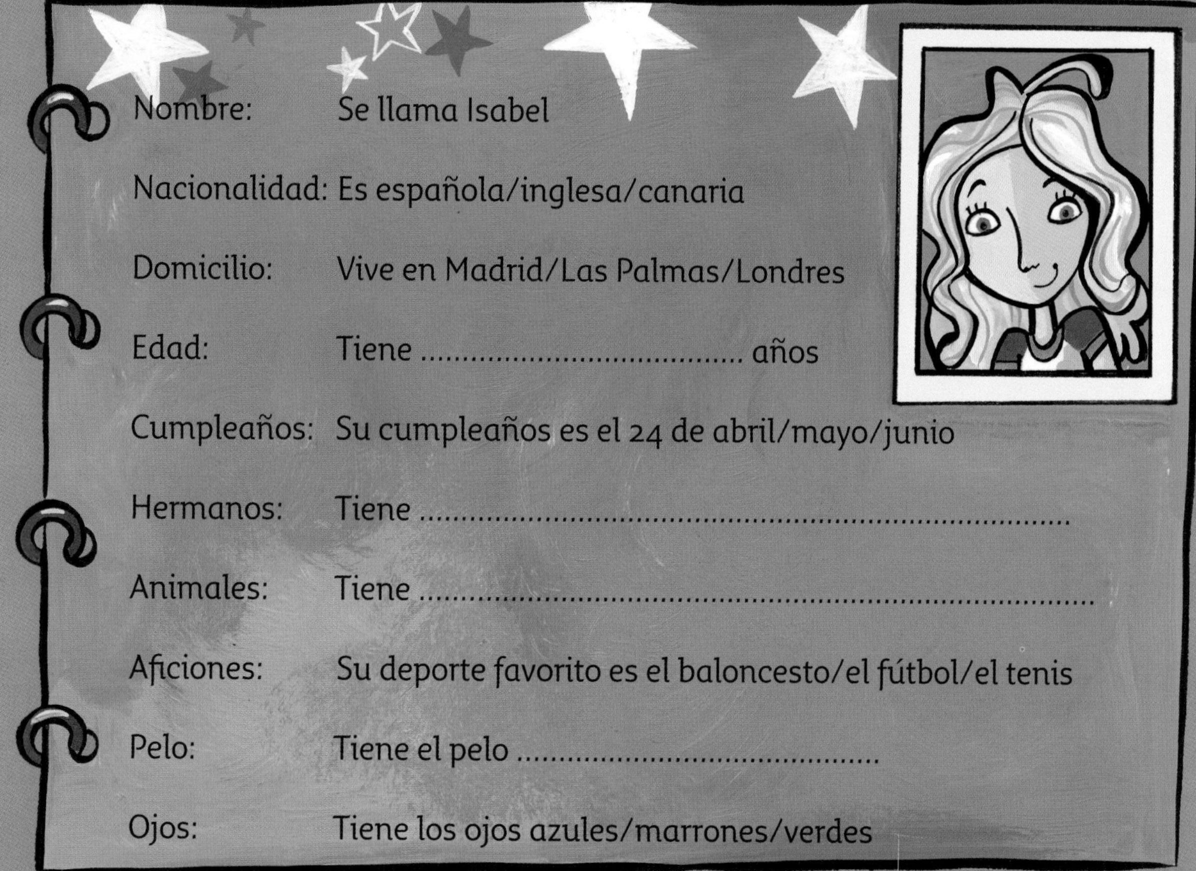

Nombre: Se llama Isabel

Nacionalidad: Es española/inglesa/canaria

Domicilio: Vive en Madrid/Las Palmas/Londres

Edad: Tiene .... años

Cumpleaños: Su cumpleaños es el 24 de abril/mayo/junio

Hermanos: Tiene ....

Animales: Tiene ....

Aficiones: Su deporte favorito es el baloncesto/el fútbol/el tenis

Pelo: Tiene el pelo ....

Ojos: Tiene los ojos azules/marrones/verdes

¿Lo sabías?

Isabel is from Las Palmas de Gran Canaria, one of the two main cities of the Canary Islands. The other main city is Santa Cruz de Tenerife. The Canary Islands are considered the southernmost part of Europe as they are situated off the coast of East Africa.

Mini Diccionario

Tiene los ojos azules/marrones/verdes.
(S)he has blue/brown/green eyes.

Tiene media melena/el pelo corto/el pelo largo.
(S)he has shoulder-length hair/short hair/long hair.

Tiene el pelo rubio/castaño/negro.
(S)he has blond/brown/black hair.

¿Y yo? Tengo los ojos .... y el pelo ....

¿Quién es?
Who is it?

Key word
¿Tiene...? Does (s)he have...?

Isabel y Jorge juegan. ¿De quién hablan?
Isabel and Jorge are playing a game. Who are they describing?

1.
Isabel: ¿Es un chico?
Jorge: Sí.
Isabel: ¿Tiene media melena?
Jorge: No.
Isabel: ¿Tiene el pelo negro?
Jorge: Sí.
Isabel: ¿Tiene los ojos marrones?
Jorge: Sí.
Isabel: ¿Lleva un sombrero?
Jorge: No.

¿Quién es?
Who is it?

Es ....

2.
Jorge: ¿Es un chico?
Isabel: No.
Jorge: ¿Tiene el pelo largo?
Isabel: Sí.
Jorge: ¿Tiene el pelo rubio?
Isabel: No.
Jorge: ¿Tiene los ojos marrones?
Isabel: Sí.
Jorge: ¿Lleva gafas?
Isabel: Sí.

¿Quién es?
Who is it?

Es ....

Truco
When you're talking about someone having glasses, a hat, a moustache or a beard you can say *tiene* (he/she has) or *lleva* (he/she is wearing).

Key phrases
¿Tiene los ojos marrones/azules/verdes? Does (s)he have brown/blue/green eyes?
¿Tiene el pelo rizado/ondulado/liso? Does (s)he have curly/wavy/straight hair?
¿Tiene el pelo rubio/gris/marrón/negro? Does (s)he have blond/grey/brown/black hair?
¿Es pelirrojo/a? Does (s)he have red hair?
¿Tiene bigote/barba? / ¿Lleva bigote/barba? Does he have a moustache/beard?
¿Lleva gafas/un sombrero? / ¿Tiene gafas/un sombero? Is (s)he wearing glasses/a hat?

Escucha a Martina y Ana jugando al juego y descubre quién es

Listen to Martina and Ana playing the game and find out who it is

Track 3

1. ....
2. ....

Escucha las descripciones de los niños del *Spanish Club*. Escribe el nombre correcto debajo de cada imagen

Listen to the descriptions of the Spanish Club kids. Write the correct name under each picture

Track 4

Lucas   Martina   Felipe
Ana   Isabel
Jorge

1. ....
2. ....
3. ....
4. ....
5. ....
6. ....

Track 5

¡Trabalenguas!

El perro persigue al pájaro

The dog chases the bird

TONGUE TWISTER

MI FAMILIA

2. My family

Track 6

"Mi madre se llama Cristina y tiene el pelo castaño. Mi padre se llama Francisco pero mi madre le llama Paco. Mis padres tienen 45 años. Mi hermano, Daniel, tiene trece años. Tiene el pelo rubio y rizado. Mi hermana, Luisa, tiene cuatro años. Tiene el pelo largo y es pelirroja. Mi tío, Antonio, lleva bigote y mi tía, Elena, tiene el pelo negro. Mi primo, Luís, tiene los ojos verdes y mi prima, Laura, lleva gafas rosas. Tengo dos abuelos, la abuela Flora y el abuelo Alberto."
Lucas

Key words

el padre father
la madre mother
el hermano brother
la hermana sister
el abuelo grandfather
la abuela grandfather
el tío uncle
la tía aunt
el primo cousin (male)
la prima cousin (female)

¿Quién es?
Who is it?

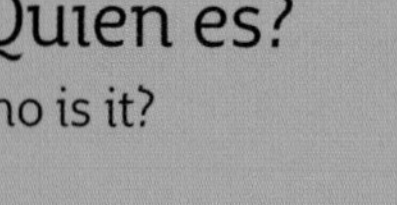

1. .... 2. .... 3. .... 4. .... 5. ....

¡El detective!

Did you notice?

The words *mi* and *mis* are both used to mean 'my'. We use *mi* with singular nouns and *mis* with plural nouns. This rule also applies to *su* (his, her or their) and *tu* (your).

mi hermana	(my sister)	*su primo*	(his/her/their cousin)
mis tíos	(my uncles)	*sus padres*	(his/her/their parents)

Mi árbol genealógico

My family tree

Escribe sus nombres debajo de las imágenes

Write their names under the pictures

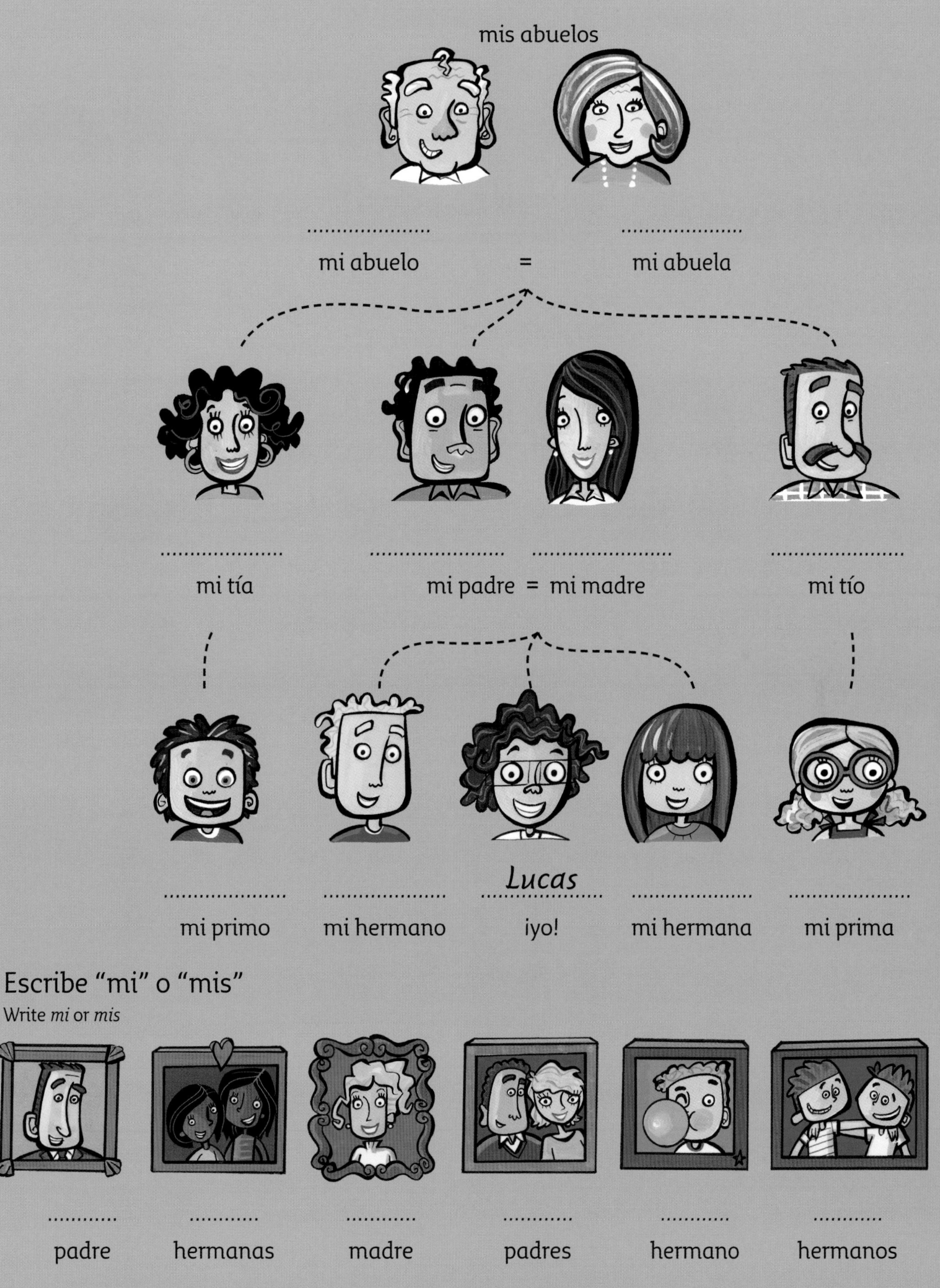

¿Quién habla?

Who is speaking?

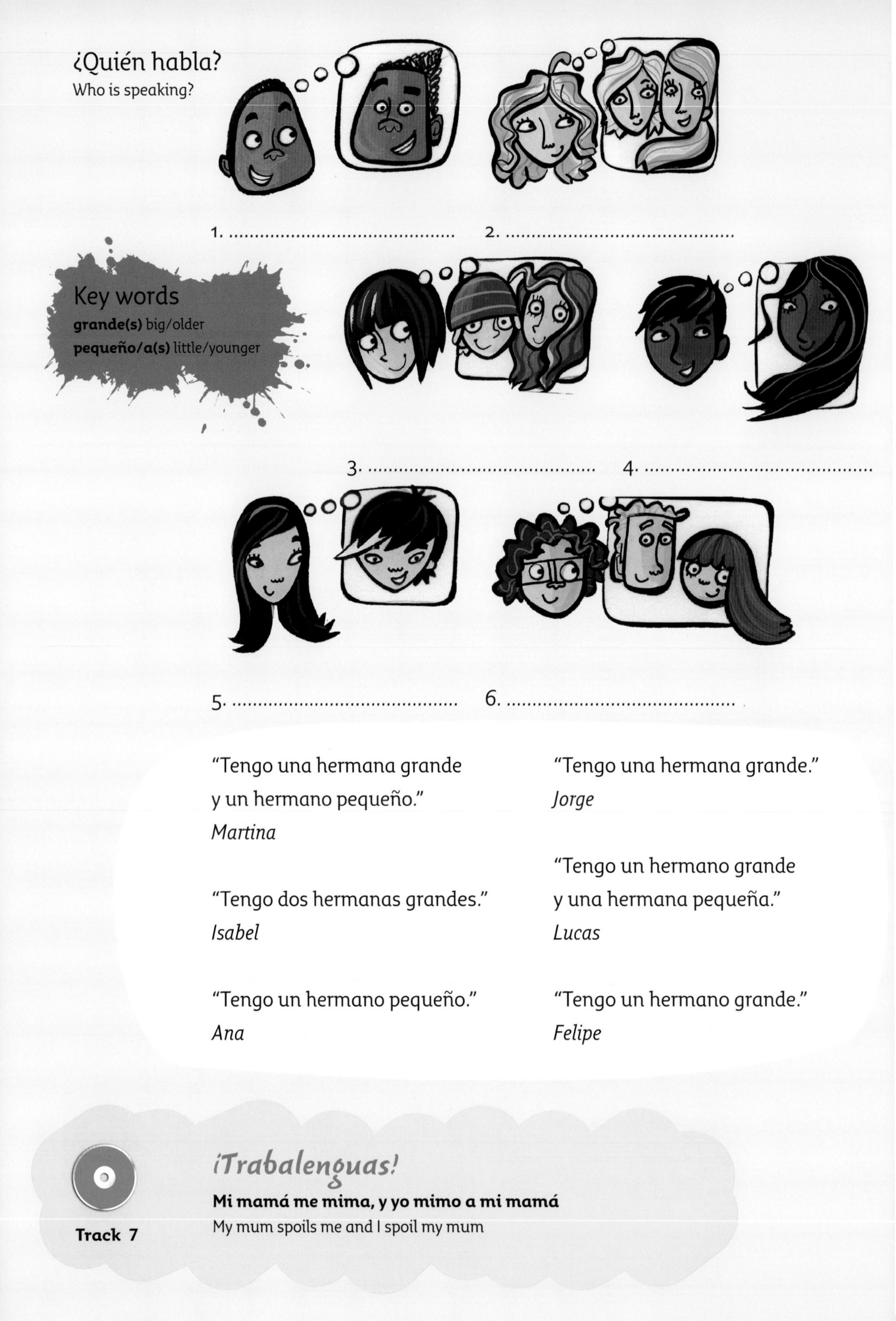

1. ....
2. ....
3. ....
4. ....
5. ....
6. ....

Key words

grande(s) big/older

pequeño/a(s) little/younger

"Tengo una hermana grande y un hermano pequeño."
Martina

"Tengo dos hermanas grandes."
Isabel

"Tengo un hermano pequeño."
Ana

"Tengo una hermana grande."
Jorge

"Tengo un hermano grande y una hermana pequeña."
Lucas

"Tengo un hermano grande."
Felipe

¡Trabalenguas!

Track 7

Mi mamá me mima, y yo mimo a mi mamá

My mum spoils me and I spoil my mum

Dibuja tu árbol genealógico

Draw your own family tree

Truco

If you don't know the word for something, why not look it up online? There is a dictionary to help you at www.collinslanguage.com. Type in the English word and it will give you the Spanish. Easy!

La familia de un rey

The family of a king

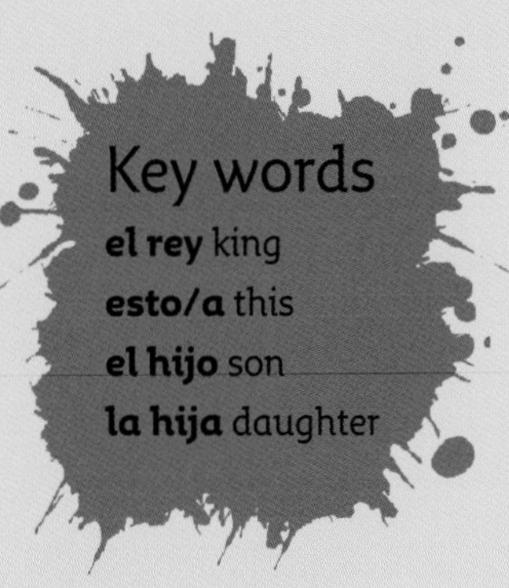

¡Hola! Soy Fernando II.
Esta es mi familia:

Mis abuelos, Fernando I
y Leonor Urraca

Mis padres, Juan II
y Juana Enríquez

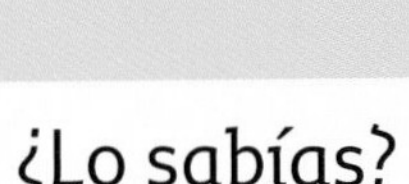

¿Lo sabías?

Fernando II was king of Aragon, Valencia and a number of other regions between 1474 and 1516. At that time, Spain was divided into various territories, so, rather than having one monarch as they do today, each area was ruled by a different king or queen.

Mi hermana, Juana

Tengo cinco hijos: Isabel, Juan, Juana, María y Catalina

Fernando's daughter Juana was known as *Juana la Loca* (Juana the Mad) because she lost her mind after the death of her husband, *Felipe el Hermoso* (Felipe the Handsome). When she became queen of Castile, Fernando II had to 'mind' the throne for her!

Fernando's five children shown here were all with his first wife, Isabel. His marriage to Isabel was a strong one and between them they controlled vast regions. When Isabel died, Fernando married again and, between his two wives and his mistresses, Fernando fathered twelve children!

Completa el texto con "mi" o "mis"

Complete the text with *mi* or *mis*

Juan II es .... padre y Juana Enríquez es .... madre.

.... abuelos se llaman Fernando I y Leonor Urraca.

.... hermana se llama Juana. Tengo cuatro hijas que se llaman Isabel, Juana, María y Catalina. .... hijo se llama Juan como yo.

Fernando

3. At home

La casa

The house

¿Quién vive dónde? Relaciona las 'personas' con sus casas

Who lives where? Link the 'people' with their houses

Key words

una casa a house
un piso a flat
un apartamento an apartment
un edificio a building
un edificio de apartamentos a block of flats

Colorea la casa de Felipe

Colour in Felipe's house

Key words

vivo I live
en la costa on the coast
en el Caribe in the Caribbean
típico/a typical; traditional
variedad variety

"Hola, soy Felipe. Vivo en la República Dominicana, en el Caribe. Vivo en una casa en la costa. Mi casa es muy típica del Caribe. El tejado es rojo, el balcón es blanco, las paredes son amarillas y las persianas son azules. La puerta es verde. Me encanta la variedad de colores."

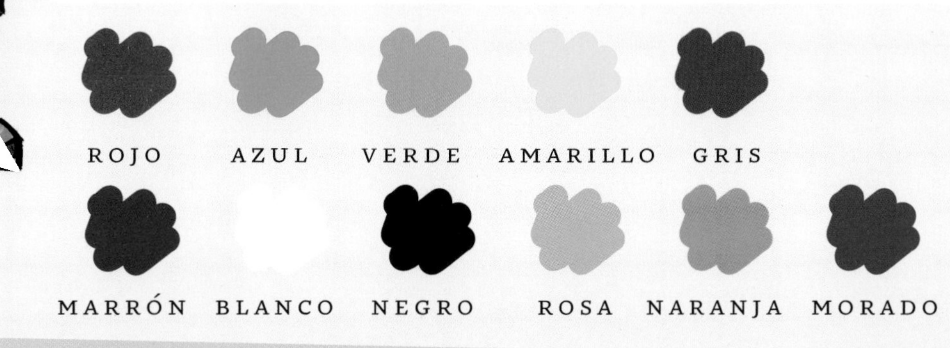

¿Lo sabías?

The Dominican Republic is a Spanish-speaking country in the Caribbean. Columbus claimed the Dominican Republic as a Spanish territory when he arrived there over 500 years ago and, despite periods of French and American rule over the years, Spanish is still the official language, although some English and Haitian Creole French is also spoken. The mixture of European and indigenous influences in the Dominican Republic has resulted in a rich culture. Colourful houses, brightly patterned clothes, lively music, energetic dance and spicy food are all important parts of Caribbean culture today.

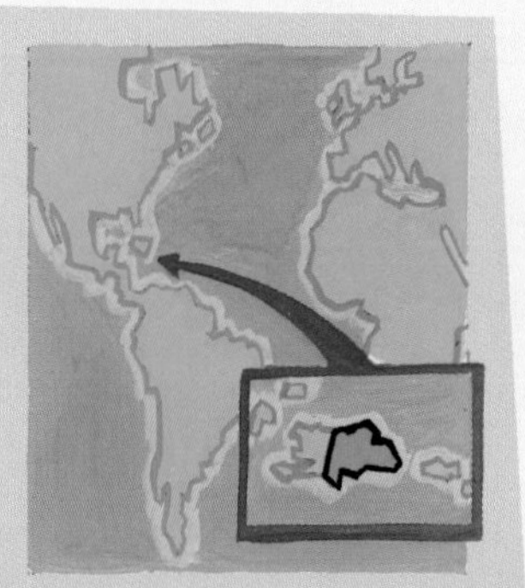

¿Cómo es tu casa? Dibuja y nombra las partes de tu casa

What's your house like? Draw and label the parts of your house

Mi castillo

My castle

Key words

en casa at home
hay there is/are

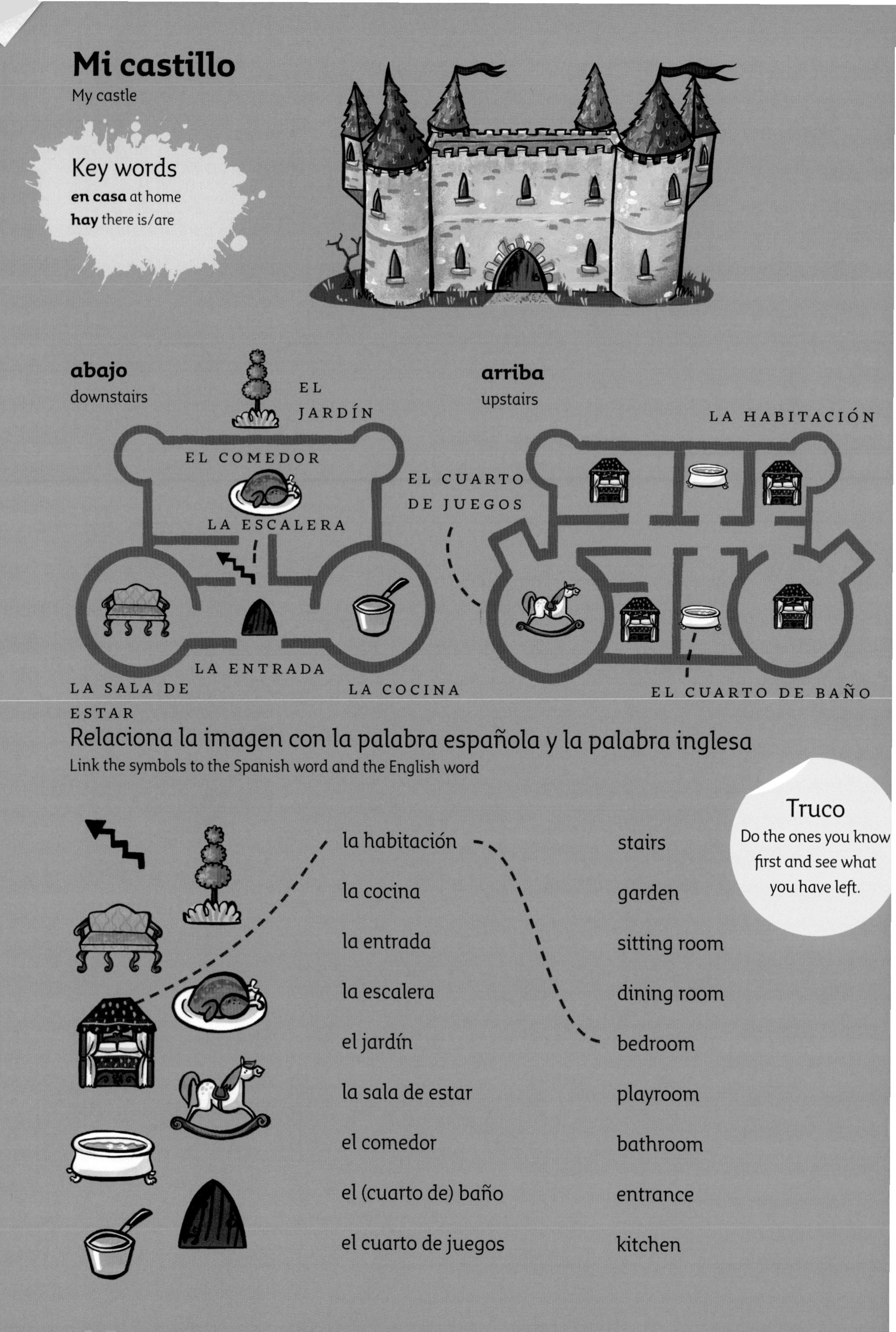

Relaciona la imagen con la palabra española y la palabra inglesa

Link the symbols to the Spanish word and the English word

la habitación	stairs
la cocina	garden
la entrada	sitting room
la escalera	dining room
el jardín	bedroom
la sala de estar	playroom
el comedor	bathroom
el (cuarto de) baño	entrance
el cuarto de juegos	kitchen

Truco

Do the ones you know first and see what you have left.

¿Qué hay detrás de la puerta?

What's behind the door?

el garaje

el cuarto de baño

la sala de estar

la habitación

la cocina

el cuarto de juegos

1 ....

2 ....

3 ....

4 ....

5 ....

6 ....

Completa el texto y dibuja un plano de tu casa

Complete the text and draw a plan of your house

Truco

Just as we can say 'living room' and 'lounge', in Spanish you can say either *el salón* or *la sala de estar.*

En mi casa hay ....

....

Mi casa ideal

My ideal house

Track 8

"Mi casa ideal está situada en la playa.

En la planta de abajo hay una cocina grande y un salón grande con un televisor. Hay una sala grande para jugar a los videojuegos y al ordenador. No hay comedor porque comemos en la cocina.

En la planta de arriba hay cinco habitaciones con sus cuartos de baño, ducha y jacuzzi.

En el sótano hay un cuarto de juegos con una mesa de ping-pong, un garaje para mis coches y bicicletas, y una despensa para las bebidas.

En el jardín hay una pista de baloncesto y una pista de tenis. Hay una piscina climatizada con un tobogán, y un área de juego con columpios.

¡Es perfecta!"

Key words

en la planta de abajo on the ground floor
el televisor television
no hay there isn't/aren't
en la planta de arriba on the first floor
en el sótano in the basement
en el jardín in the garden
la despensa storage room
una bebida drink

Escucha el CD. ¿Qué quiere tener Ana en su casa?

Listen to the CD. What does Ana want to have in her house?

Track 9

✓

¿Qué quieres tú tener en tu casa?

What do you want to have in your house?

Dibuja un plano de tu casa ideal y completa el texto

Draw a plan of your ideal house and complete the text

Mi casa ideal está situada en ....

Es (un piso / una casa). Abajo hay ....

....

Arriba hay ....

En el sótano hay ....

En el jardín hay ....

Mini Diccionario

la playa beach
el campo countryside
la gran ciudad city
la ciudad town
el pueblo village
las montañas mountains

Track 10

¡Trabalenguas!

Camila come comida en el comedor
Camila eats food in the dining room

ESPAÑA

4. Spain

¿Es español o no?

Is it Spanish or not?

Key phrases

Es español/a It's Spanish

No es español/a It isn't Spanish

Marca con un círculo las cosas españolas

Circle the Spanish things

Truco

If you can't think of three things or three people, why not go on the internet and find out some more about Spain?

¿Puedes nombrar tres cosas españolas?

Can you name three things that are Spanish?

....

¿Puedes nombrar tres personajes españoles?

Can you name three Spanish people?

....

Recorta y pega, o dibuja las cosas españolas y escribe sus nombres

Cut out and stick, or draw some Spanish things and write their names

¡El detective!

Did you notice?

In Spanish, you simply add *no* before the verb to make a sentence negative.

Es español (It's Spanish)
***No** es español* (It isn't Spanish)

En Madrid

In Madrid

¿Lo sabías?

Madrid is the capital of Spain. It is situated in the centre of Spain and has many famous buildings, squares and museums. The river Manzanares runs through the city.

Key places

El Palacio Real The Royal Palace, built by Felipe V, is not home to today's royal family but is open to the public.

La Plaza Mayor A huge square where many bullfights, coronations, executions, markets and concerts were held. Now it is a popular place to meet friends, soak up the atmosphere and enjoy a coffee in one of the many outdoor cafés.

El Parque del Buen Retiro Madrid's largest park where you can hire a rowing boat and paddle around the lake.

La Puerta del Sol A bustling square generally seen to be the centre of the city. The symbol of Madrid, a bear eating fruit from a tree, stands proudly in the middle.

La Catedral de la Almudena A beautiful cathedral opposite the palace where Prince Felipe and Princess Letizia got married in 2004.

La Gran Vía A busy avenue in central Madrid with hotels, souvenir shops and cinemas.

La Plaza de España A square with a sculpture of the Spanish writer Miguel de Cervantes, and his famous Don Quixote and Sancho Panza characters.

El Estadio Santiago Bernabéu The Real Madrid football stadium which seats about 80 thousand people.

El Museo del Prado A huge museum which houses some of the finest art collections in the world.

La Estación de Atocha The biggest train station in Spain. It is in the south of Madrid and has a large dome in the centre.

Busca los sitios en el mapa y escribe el número

Find the places on the plan and write down the number

El Palacio Real .... La Plaza Mayor .... El Parque del Buen Retiro ....

La Puerta del Sol .... La Gran Vía .... La Catedral de la Almudena ....

El Estadio Santiago Bernabéu .... La Plaza de España ....

El Museo del Prado .... La Estación de Atocha ....

Relaciona las imágenes con los sitios

Match the pictures with the places

la Gran Vía

la Plaza de España

el Museo del Prado

la Estación de Atocha

el Parque del Buen Retiro

el Palacio Real

la Plaza Mayor

la Catedral de la Almudena

el Estadio Santiago Bernabéu

la Puerta del Sol

Truco

Do the ones you understand first and then see what you have left.

Track 11

¡Trabalenguas!

Mi madre es de Madrid

My mother is from Madrid

¿Dónde viven?

Where do they live?

La brújula

The compass

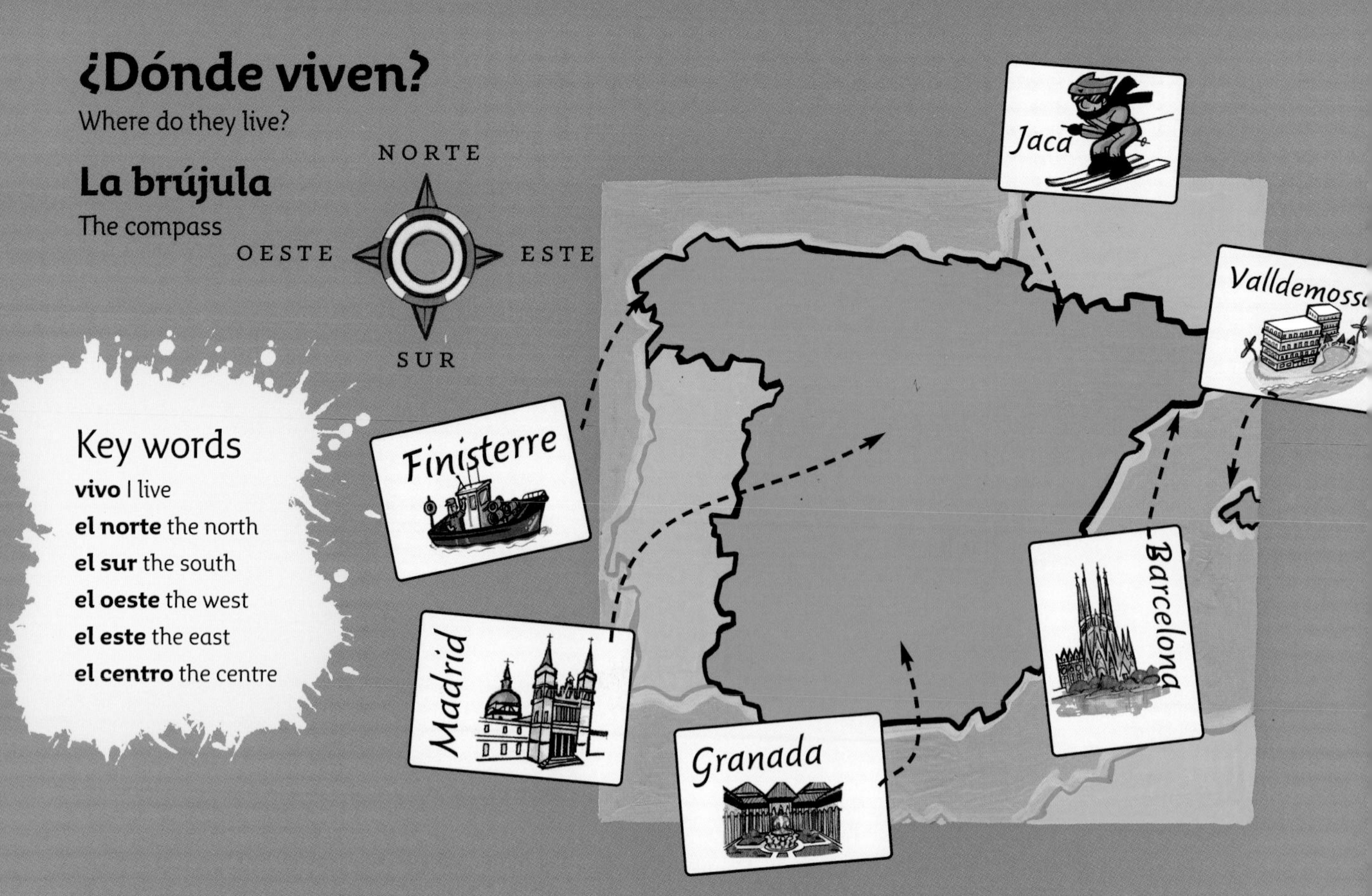

Key words

vivo I live
el norte the north
el sur the south
el oeste the west
el este the east
el centro the centre

Encuentra los sitios en el mapa y escribe las palabras en los espacios

Find the places and write the names in the gaps

MARTINA: Es una ciudad histórica en el sur cerca de las montañas de Sierra Nevada. Vivo en ....

PEDRO: Es un pueblo en la costa en Mallorca en las Islas Baleares. Vivo en ....

BERTA: Es un pueblo de esquí en las montañas del norte de España – los Pirineos. Vivo en ....

ANA: Es la capital de España y está situada en el centro del país. Vivo en ....

JUAN: Es un pequeño pueblo de pesca en Galicia, en el oeste de España. Vivo en ....

Es una ciudad muy grande en la costa mediterránea, en el este de España. Vivo en ....

¿Dónde vives?
Where do you live?

Vivo en .... en el (norte / sur / oeste / este / centro) de ....

Es un (pueblo / ciudad) (grande / pequeño/a).

Truco
New words? Look for connections! Some words look or sound almost the same in English: *costa* (coast); *puerto* (port); *norte* (north); *oeste* (west).

¿Qué más puedes decir sobre tu casa?
What else can you say about your home town in Spanish?

....

¿Dónde viven? Escucha el CD y marca la casilla correspondiente
Where do they live? Listen and tick the correct boxes

Track 12

	small	big	town	city	north	south	east	west	centre
Alberto		✓		✓	✓				
Marta									
Ricardo									
Sara									
Enrique									
Raquel									
José									
Eva									

¿CÓMO SON?

5. What are they like?

Key words

más more
más grande que bigger than
más pequeño/a que smaller than
el/la más grande the biggest
el/la más pequeño/a the smallest

¿Más grande o más pequeño/a?

Bigger or smaller?

Soy más grande que Luisa

Soy más pequeña que Lucas

Soy más grande que Antonio

Soy más pequeño que Ana

Truco

Remember to use *pequeña* if you are referring to a female. The word *grande* stays the same for males and females.

¡El detective!

Did you remember?

Spanish doesn't have -er and -est to compare things like English does. Instead, they always say 'more ...' and 'the most ...'.

guapa (pretty) *más guapa* (prettier) *la más guapa* (the prettiest)

Completa los bocadillos

Complete the speech bubbles

¿Cómo se llaman los hijos del rey?

What are the king's children called?

Key words

mayor older
el/la mayor the oldest
menor younger
el/la menor the youngest

¡Hola! Soy Juan Carlos, el rey de España. Tengo tres hijos. Elena es la mayor. Felipe es el menor. Cristina es mayor que Felipe y menor que Elena.

1. ....
2. ....
3. ....

¿Es tímido/a?

Is he/she shy?

¿Cómo son? Relaciona las palabras con las imágenes

What are they like? Join the words to the pictures

Key words

hablador(a) chatty
deportista sporty
gracioso/a funny
guapo/a handsome/pretty
inteligente clever
simpático/a nice
tímido/a shy

1.
2.
3.
4.
5.
6.

deportista

inteligente

graciosa

hablador

guapa

habladora

¡El detective!

Did you notice?

Some adjectives (describing words) change depending on whether they are referring to a male or female.

If the adjective ends in *-o* it can normally change to an *-a*.
If the adjective ends in *-r* you simply add *-a*.

masculine	feminine	
pequeñ**o**	pequeñ**a**	(small)
gracios**o**	gracios**a**	(funny)
guap**o**	guap**a**	(good looking)
hablado**r**	hablador**a**	(chatty)

Some adjectives stay the same when describing males and females.

grand**e** (big)   inteligent**e** (clever)   deportist**a** (sporty)

Escucha y relaciona las personas con las palabras
Listen to the CD and match the people with the words

Track 13

Rita
Paco
Mateo
Benito
Miriam
Alejandro
Claudio
Julia
Jorge
María

guapo
inteligente
simpático
graciosa
deportista
habladora
guapa
gracioso
deportista
tímido

Mi familia
My family

Encuentra a alguien en tu familia que sea...
Find someone in your family who is...

deportista ....

inteligente ....

gracioso ....

guapa ....

tímida ....

hablador ....

simpática ....

Y tú, ¿cómo eres?
And you, what are you like?

Yo soy ....

No es tímido/a

He/she is not shy

Key words

(yo) no soy I'm not
(él) no es he isn't
(ella) no es she isn't

¡El detective!

Did you notice?

To make a Spanish sentence negative, simply add *no* before the verb. 'Negative' means there is a 'no' or a 'not' in the sentence. Instead of talking about what you are, you are talking about what you are not:

I am **not** ten years old   I do **not** have a dog   I do **not** like maths

(yo) soy	(I am)	(yo) hablo mucho	(I talk a lot)
(él) es	(he is)	(él) habla mucho	(he talks a lot)
(ella) es	(she is)	(ella) habla mucho	(she talks a lot)
(yo) **no** soy	(I'm not)	(yo) **no** hablo mucho	(I don't talk a lot)
(él) **no** es	(he isn't)	(él) **no** habla mucho	(he doesn't talk a lot)
(ella) **no** es	(she isn't)	(ella) **no** habla mucho	(she doesn't talk a lot)

No soy habladora
I am not talkative

Lucas no es deportista
Lucas isn't sporty

JOKE

¡Chiste!

Track 14

Una madre a su hijo:	A mother to her son:
¿Qué haces?	What are you doing?
Nada.	*Nothing.*
¿Y tu hermano pequeño?	And your little brother?
¡Me ayuda!	*He's helping me!*

¿Cómo son? ¿Verdadero (v) o falso (f)?

What are they like? True (v) or false (f)?

"En mi clase mi amiga Marta es muy habladora. Habla mucho. Juan no es hablador pero es más deportista que Marta. Mi amiga Elena es la más inteligente. Clara es guapa pero es demasiado tímida. Leticia no es tímida. Es muy simpática. Bernardo es mucho más tímido. No habla nunca. ¿Y yo? Yo soy el más hablador. Hablo muchísimo!" *Jorge*

Marta es tímida ..F.......   Juan es deportista ....

Elena es inteligente ....   Clara es guapa ....   Leticia no es simpática ....

Jorge es tímido ....   Bernardo es hablador ....

Ahora escucha a Jorge hablando de sus amigos

Now listen to Jorge telling you about his friends. Can you hear the differences between the female and male endings?

Mini Diccionario

mi amigo/a my friend
muy very
demasiado too (much)
también too (also)
un poco a bit
nunca never
muchísimo a lot
quién who

Mis amigos

My friends

¿Quién es el más tímido? ....   ¿Quién no habla nunca? ....

¿Quién es la más simpática? ....   ¿Quién es la más guapa? ....

¿Quién es la más deportista? ....   ¿Quién no es conversador? ....

¿Quién es la más inteligente? ....   ¿Quién habla muchísimo? ....

Truco

Look for clues to see if you need to think of a male or a female friend, but sometimes it could be either!

m	f
el** más tímid**o	***la** más simpátic**a***

¡Mi perro es mi amigo más simpático!

Mi día

6. My day

La mañana

The morning

Key words

me levanto I get up
me lavo I get washed
me visto I get dressed

Truco

In Spanish, instead of saying *I get washed* and *I get dressed* you say *I wash myself* and *I dress myself*. Verbs that do this are called **reflexive verbs**.

Son las siete

Me levanto

Me lavo

Me visto

Son las siete y media

Bajo a la cocina

Desayuno

Me lavo los dientes

Son las ocho

Me pongo la chaqueta

Cojo mi mochila

Salgo

Completa las frases

Complete the sentence

¿A qué hora?

What time?

Dibuja las manecillas en los relojes

Draw the hands on the clocks

1. Son las tres

2. Es mediodía

3. Son las ocho y media

Mini Diccionario

1 **un(o/a)**
2 **dos**
3 **tres**
4 **cuatro**
5 **cinco**
6 **seis**
7 **siete**
8 **ocho**
9 **nueve**
10 **diez**
11 **once**
12 **doce**
mediodía midday
medianoche midnight
y media half past
y cuarto quarter past
menos cuarto quarter to

4. Son las cinco

5. Son las nueve y cuarto

6. Son las once menos cuarto

7. Es medianoche

Lina vive en Nicaragua

Lina lives in Nicaragua

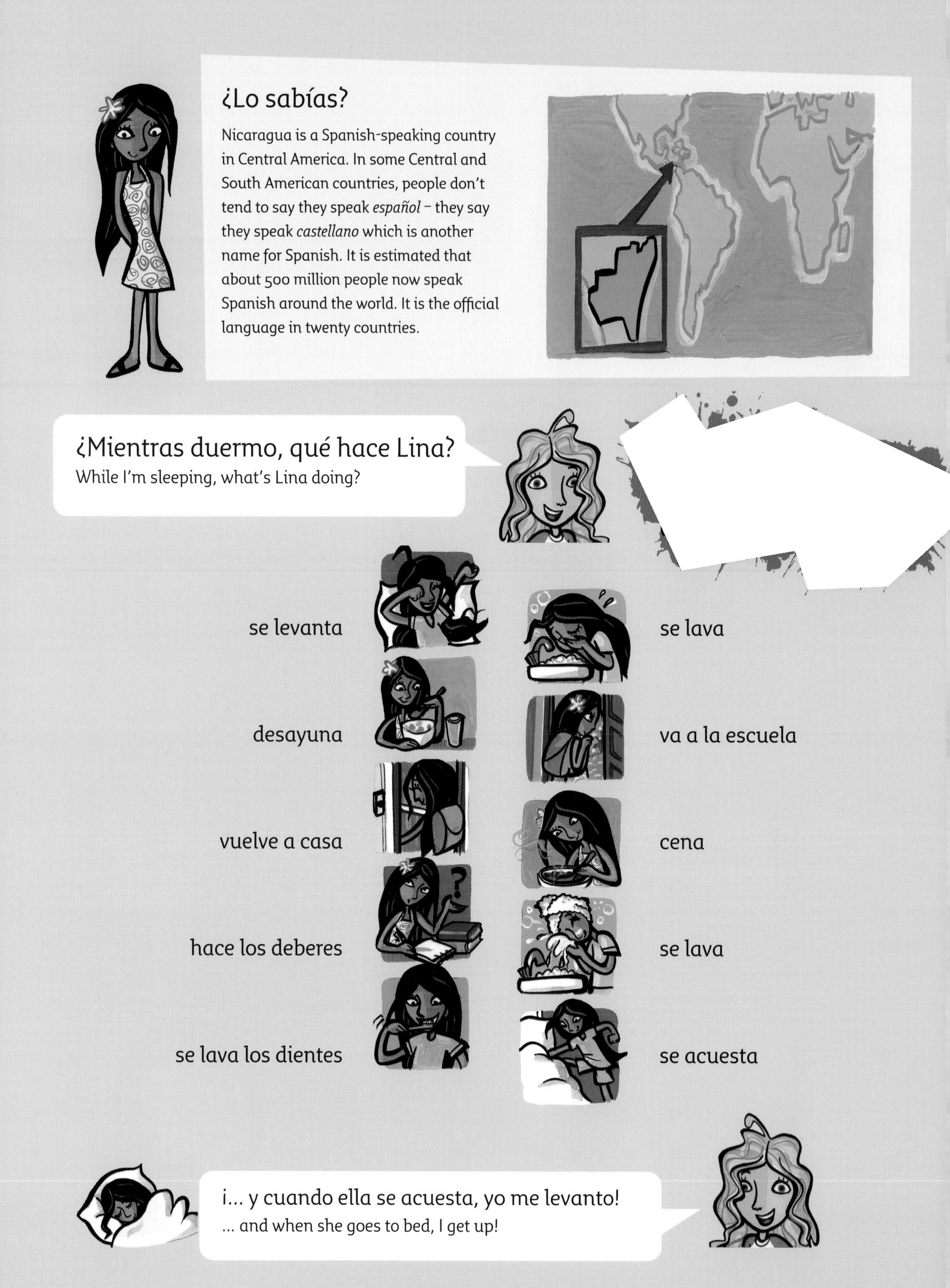

¿Lo sabías?

Nicaragua is a Spanish-speaking country in Central America. In some Central and South American countries, people don't tend to say they speak *español* – they say they speak *castellano* which is another name for Spanish. It is estimated that about 500 million people now speak Spanish around the world. It is the official language in twenty countries.

¿Mientras duermo, qué hace Lina?

While I'm sleeping, what's Lina doing?

se levanta

se lava

desayuna

va a la escuela

vuelve a casa

cena

hace los deberes

se lava

se lava los dientes

se acuesta

¡... y cuando ella se acuesta, yo me levanto!

... and when she goes to bed, I get up!

¡El detective!

Did you notice?

Lots of the words used in this unit have *se* before them. *Se* means 'himself' or 'herself'.

se levanta (she gets herself up)
se lava (she washes herself)

These verbs are called reflexive verbs. When you look up a reflexive verb in the dictionary, it will look like this:

lavar**se** (to wash yourself) levantar**se** (to get up)

This is the infinitive, the basic form of the verb. When you use verbs you have to think about who or what is doing the action and change the ending of the infinitive to make it fit.

Use *me* when talking about yourself and *te* if you want to say 'you'

me lavo (I wash myself) **te** lavas (you wash yourself)

Key words

despertarse to wake up
desayunar to have breakfast
ir a la escuela to go to school
volver a casa to go home
hacer los deberes to do your homework
salir to go out
llegar to arrive
acostarse to go to bed

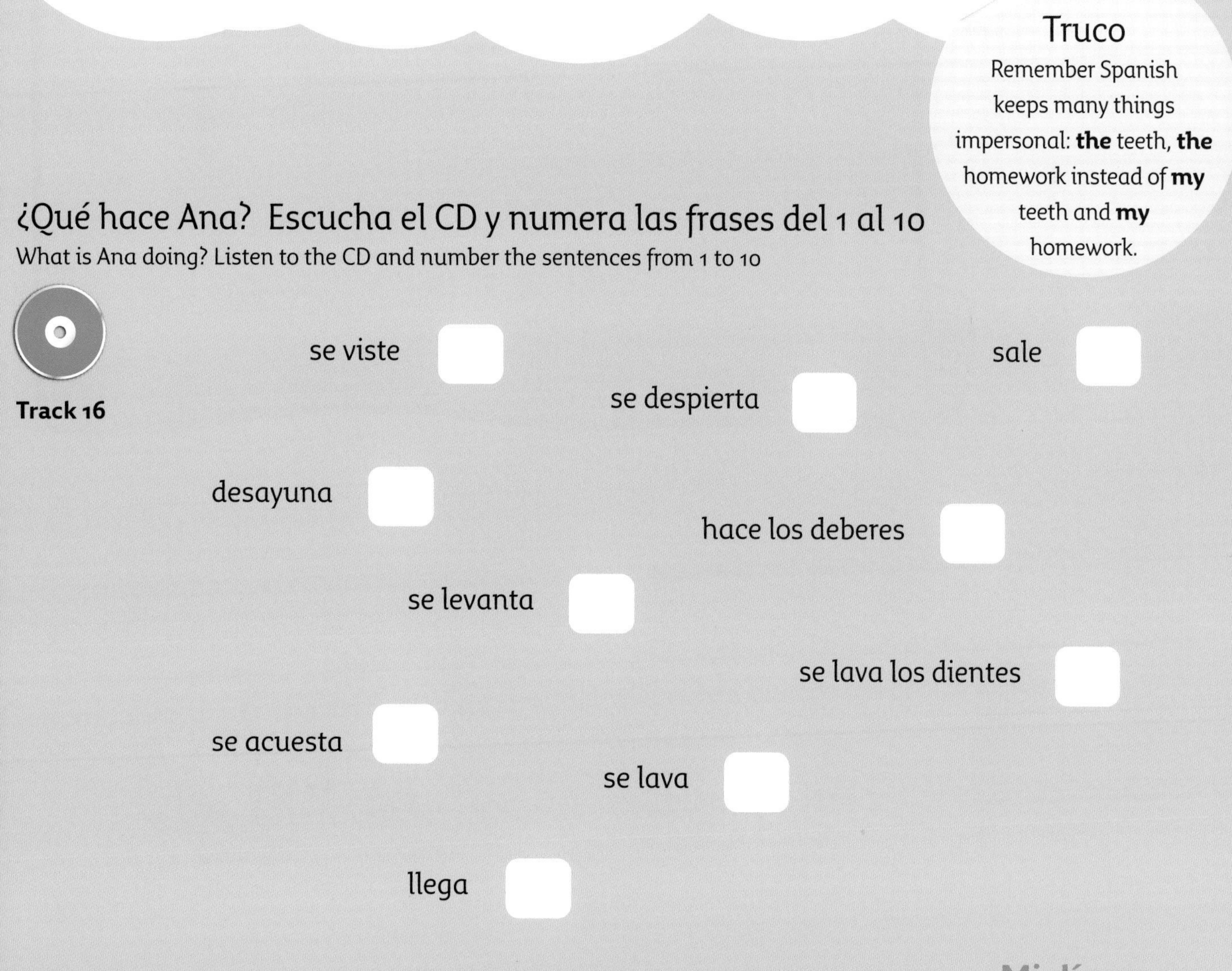

Truco

Remember Spanish keeps many things impersonal: **the** teeth, **the** homework instead of **my** teeth and **my** homework.

¿Qué hace Ana? Escucha el CD y numera las frases del 1 al 10

What is Ana doing? Listen to the CD and number the sentences from 1 to 10

Track 16

se viste ☐
sale ☐
se despierta ☐
desayuna ☐
hace los deberes ☐
se levanta ☐
se lava los dientes ☐
se acuesta ☐
se lava ☐
llega ☐

El día del rey Fernando

King Fernando's day

La mañana

8h El rey se despierta

8h15 Se levanta

8h30 Se lava

9h Desayuna

9h30 Se viste

10h Va a la iglesia

11h Se reune com sus consejeros

11h30 Descansa

La tarde

14h Almuerza

15h30 Va de caza o va a montar a caballo

17h Se viste para la noche

La noche

18h Baila, escucha música o juega a las cartas o al billar

22h Cena

23h Se acuesta

Mini Diccionario

va a la iglesia he goes to church
se reune con sus consejeros he meets with his advisors
descansa he takes a rest
va a cazar he goes hunting
va a montar a caballo he goes horseriding
baila he dances
juega a las cartas/al billar he plays cards/billiards
escucha música he listens to music

¿Lo sabías?

Even though it is not clear whether Christopher Columbus was actually Spanish, he famously discovered the Americas under Isabella and Fernando's reign. This was probably the most powerful era in Spanish history.

¿Y tú? ¿Qué haces tú?

And you? What do you do?

La mañana ....

....

La tarde ....

....

La noche ....

....

Truco
Use a dictionary or go online to www.collinslanguage.com to find all the words you need.

¡El detective!

Did you notice?

When you look up a verb in a dictionary or online, it is given in the *infinitive form*. In Spanish, most infinitives end in *-ar*.

jug**ar** (to play) bail**ar** (to dance) cen**ar** (to have dinner)

Many others end in *-er* or *-ir*.

volv**er** (to return) eleg**ir** (to choose) vest**ir**se (to get dressed)

If you want to adapt the verb so you can say what *you* are doing, replace the *-ar*, *-er* or *-ir* ending with *-o*.

bail**ar** – bail**o** (I dance) cen**ar** – cen**o** (I eat dinner)

Sometimes the middle of the verb changes too. These are called *irregular verbs*:

j**u**gar – j**ue**go v**o**lver – v**ue**lvo el**eg**ir – el**ij**o v**e**stirse – me v**i**sto

Some verbs are completely irregular, meaning that the whole word changes:

ir (to go) – voy I go
ser/estar (to be) – soy/estoy (I am)
tener (to have) – tengo (I have)

Truco
Try to remember these three irregular verbs because you will use them a lot.

Track 17

¡Trabalenguas!

El rey se ríe de la reina
The king laughs at the queen

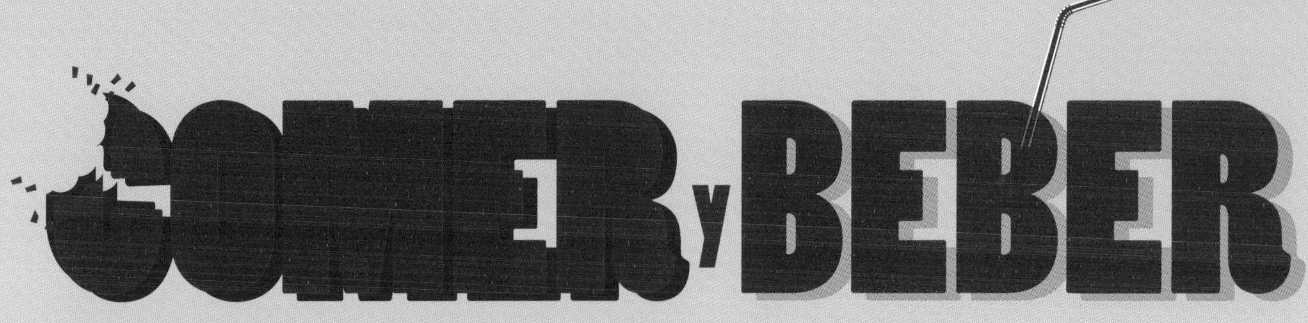

7. Eating and drinking

Key words
el desayuno breakfast
comer to eat
beber to drink

El desayuno

Breakfast

Marca con un círculo los alimentos que comes y bebes en el desayuno

Circle the things you eat and drink for breakfast

¿Lo sabías?

Most Spanish children have two breakfasts! Many kids have toast or a bowl of cereal before they leave for school and then at break time they have a 'proper breakfast' which is usually a large sandwich with cheese or cold meat.

¿De quién es el desayuno?

Whose is the breakfast?

1. .... 2. .... 3. .... 4. ....

Como un yogur, una tostada con mermelada y bebo zumo de naranja.

ANA

MARTINA

Como cereales con leche, una tostada con miel y bebo zumo de piña.

Como pan con aceite, jamón y queso, y bebo café.

ISABEL

FELIPE

Como cereales con leche, pan con crema de chocolate, y un plátano, y bebo chocolate caliente.

Escucha el CD. ¿Quién habla?

Listen to the CD. Who is speaking?

Track 18

1. .... 2. ....

3. .... 4. ....

¿Lo sabías?

Spanish people normally eat a three course meal for lunch around two o'clock that keeps them going until dinner time which is often eaten as late as ten o'clock. Children usually fit in a snack around five o'clock too!

Surprisingly, there are very few overweight Spaniards. This is due to the fresh, natural and generally healthy ingredients in their diet.

La fruta y la verdura

Fruit and vegetables

Key words

Me gusta(n) I like

No me gusta(n) I don't like

Marca con un círculo las frutas y verduras que te gustan. Tacha las que no te gustan

Circle the things you like to eat. Cross out the things you don't like to eat

la col | las zanahorias | los guisantes | el brócoli | las cebollas

la lechuga | los tomates | el pepino | las patatas | los pimientos

la berenjena | el calabacín | las manzanas | las peras | los plátanos

las naranjas | las uvas | los melocotones | la piña | el melón

Escribe una lista

Write a list

Me gusta(n) ...
I like ...

No me gusta(n) ...
I don't like ...

¡Prepárate una bebida de frutas!

Make yourself a fruit drink!

Un batido

A milkshake

Mini Diccionario

un puñado de a handful of
una fresa strawberry
una bola a ball; scoop
un poco de a bit of
o or
todo everything
frío chilled
pelar to peel
añadir to add
poner to put
triturar to blend
servir to serve

Ingredientes Ingredients

10 uvas
1 plátano
Un puñado de fresas
Una bola de helado de vainilla
Un yogur o un poco de leche

Instrucciones Instructions

Pela o lava las frutas.
Pon las frutas en la batidora.
Añade el helado, el yogur o la leche.
Tritúralo todo en la batidora.
¡Sírvelo frío!

¿Qué fruta utilizarías para preparar tu bebida perfecta?

What fruit would you use to make your perfect drink? Draw them here and write their names in Spanish

Escucha: ¿Qué helado prefieren?

Listen: Which ice cream do they like?

Track 19

El almuerzo del rey

The king's lunch

LA CARTA

APERITIVO Aperitif

Aceitunas rellenas de anchoa
Olives stuffed with anchovies

Almejas
Clams

Mejillones
Mussels

Jamón ibérico
Iberian ham

Gazpacho
Chilled tomato soup

PRIMER PLATO Starter

Tortilla española
Spanish omelette

Paella de marisco
Seafood paella

SEGUNDO PLATO Main course

Pato asado con salsa de frutas del bosque
Roast duck with fruits of the forest sauce

POSTRE Dessert

Pastel de chocolate blanco con helado de mora y
White chocolate cake with blackberry and coconut ice crear

¿Lo sabías?

This menu is quite extravagant but it could be decribed as fairly typical Spanish cuisine. Food is a very important part of Spanish culture and they value both quality and quantity.

¿Qué comes para el almuerzo?

What do you eat for lunch?

Marca con un círculo las cosas que comes y bebes. Tacha las cosas que no comes ni bebes

Circle the things you eat and drink. Cross out the things you don't eat or drink

Como ...

patatas fritas

pasta

arroz

carne

pescado

bocadillos

patatas

queso

yogur

fruta

Bebo ...

agua

cola

té

café

zumo de naranja

Ahora escribe una lista de las comidas que te gusta comer

Now write a list of some more foods that you like to eat

....

....

....

Truco

Try looking up some of your favourite foods and drinks in a dictionary or online.

Track 20

¡Chiste!

María: ¿Puedes darme un euro, mamá?	Can I have a euro, mum?
Mamá: ¿Para qué?	*Why?*
María: Para dárselo a una señora mayor.	To give to an old lady
Mamá: Eres muy buena. ¿Qué hace la señora?	*That's kind. What does she do?*
María: ¡Vende helados!	She sells ice cream!

La escuela

8. School

Voy a la escuela

I'm going to school

Track 21

Mini Diccionario

voy I go / I am going
el autobús escolar school bus
la bicicleta bicycle
a pie on foot
cuando when
el patio playground
hasta until
repaso mis deberes I check over my homework
llego I arrive
la campana suena the bell rings

"Por la mañana me levanto a las siete. Desayuno con mi hermana y mi madre. Repaso mis deberes y salgo a las ocho y diez. Voy a la escuela en bicicleta. Cuando llego, juego al fútbol en el patio con mis amigos hasta las ocho y media. La campana suena y entramos en la escuela. Decimos 'hola' a los profesores y las clases empiezan a las nueve."

JORGE

Escucha y lee: Dibuja las manecillas en los relojes

Listen and read: Draw hands on the clocks

Se levanta

Sale

Las clases empiezan

Truco

Did you notice the verbs ending in *-mos*? This is the ending used when you want to say 'we do something'.

entrar (to enter)
entramos (we enter)
decir (to say)
decimos (we say)

¿Lo sabías?

You will often see friends kissing each other when they say good morning. This 'greeting kiss' (where you kiss each other on both cheeks) is called *dos besos* (two kisses). Young people will often greet each other with *dos besos*. They will also kiss their parents and the parents of friends that they know well.

¿Qué medio de transporte es?

What means of transport is it?

Relaciona las imágenes con las palabras

Match the pictures with the words

Truco

Spanish often uses the shortened forms *bus* instead of *autobús* and *bici* instead of *bicicleta*.

¿Cómo vas a la escuela?

How do you go to school?

Voy a la escuela en

....

FELIPE

Voy a la escuela a

....

LUCAS

Voy a la escuela en

....

MARTINA

Voy a la escuela en

....

ISABEL

Voy a la escuela en

....

JORGE

Mi madre me lleva a la escuela en ....

ANA

Mini Diccionario

me lleva (she) takes me

¿A qué hora vas tú a la escuela?

Voy a la escuela a las ....

¿Cómo vas a la escuela?

Voy a la escuela ....

Escucha y lee el texto de Lucas

Listen and read Lucas's text

Track 22

Nombre: *Lucas* Fecha: *8 de junio*

"Las clases empiezan a las ocho y media. Los martes, por ejemplo, tengo matemáticas.

La hora del recreo es de las diez y cuarto hasta las once menos cuarto.

Entonces, hago ciencias. A las once y media tengo clase de inglés hasta las doce, y luego educación física hasta la una y media.

Tenemos una hora y media para comer y jugar en el patio.

A las tres tengo clase de lengua y después tengo una hora de música.

Terminamos a las cinco. Llego a casa y estoy muy cansado porque el día en la escuela es muy largo... ¡pero también es divertido!"

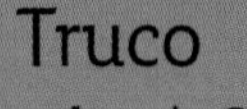

Truco

Remember that, in Spanish, you don't write the days of the week with capital letters. For the other days of the week, see page 60

Mini Diccionario

las clases classes
el recreo break
empiezan (they) begin
dura (it) lasts
terminar to finish
luego then
después after
entonces then
hasta until
acabo I finish
por ejemplo for example
los martes on Tuesdays
ciencias Science
lengua language (Spanish)
cansado/a tired
porque because
largo/a long
divertido/a fun

Las matemáticas
Maths

El día escolar
The school day

Mini Diccionario
empieza starts
termina finishes
dura(n) it/they last(s)
¿Cuánto tiempo...? How long...?

La mañana The morning

1. La clase de matemáticas empieza a las ocho y media y termina a las diez y cuarto. Dura .... minutos.
2. El recreo empieza a las diez y cuarto y termina a las once menos cuarto. Dura .... minutos.
3. La clase de lengua empieza a las once menos cuarto y termina a las once y media. Dura .... minutos.
4. La hora para comer empieza a las once y media y termina a la una y cuarto. Dura .... minutos.
5. La clase de ciencias empieza a la una y cuarto y termina a las tres. Dura .... minutos.
6. El recreo empieza a las tres y termina a las tres y media. Dura .... minutos.
7. La clase de música empieza a las tres y media y termina a las cuatro. Dura .... minutos.
8. ¿Cuánto tiempo duran las clases? Duran ....
9. ¿Cuánto tiempo duran los recreos y la hora para comer? ....
10. ¿Cuánto tiempo dura el día escolar? ....

¿Y en tu escuela?
And at your school?

¿Cuánto tiempo dura el día escolar? ....

¿Cuánto tiempo duran el recreo y la hora para comer? ....

¿Cuánto tiempo duran las clases? ....

Ciencias
Science

¿Para qué sirven? Relaciona las palabras con las definiciones
What are they for? Match the words with the definitions

los ojos	para oler
las orejas	para tocar
la nariz	para saborear
la lengua	para ver
las manos	para oír

Key words
el sentido sense
para for/in order to
oír to hear
saborear to taste
oler to smell
tocar to feel/touch
ver to see
el brazo arm
la voz voice

Completa el poema
Complete the poem

Track 23

Tengo .... para verte,
I have ... to see you,

Tengo .... para oírte,
I have ... to hear you,

Tengo .... para olerte,
I have ... to smell you,

Tengo .... para tocarte,
I have ... to touch you,

Tengo brazos para abrazarte,
I have arms to hug you,

Y una voz para recitarte un poema.
And a voice to recite a poem to you.

Truco
Did you notice the *-te* at the end of the verbs? This is another way of saying 'you'.

Can you try writing a poem?
It doesn't have to rhyme.
Some useful words:

caminar (to walk)
mirar (to watch)
cantar (to sing)
cazar (to chase)
jugar (to play)

Track 24

¡Chiste!
José: Señorita, ¿puedo estar castigado por algo que no he hecho?
José: Miss, can I be punished for something I haven't done?
Profesora: ¡Claro que no!
Teacher: Of course not!
José: Pues muy bien. ¡No he hecho mis deberes!
José: That's okay, then. I haven't done my homework!

¿Como se pronuncia?

How do you pronounce it?

Track 25

Truco

All of these words have been used in the book. Look them up in a dictionary if you can't remember what they mean.

Escucha el CD e intenta leer estas palabras lo más rápidamente posible

Listen to the CD and try to speed-read these words

c When **c** comes before an **e** or an **i**, it is pronounced like **th** in '**th**in'.
If the **c** comes before any other vowel, it is pronounced like **k** or **c** as in '**c**at'.
cinco, cocina, ciudad, como, cuatro, casa...

g When **g** comes before an **e** or an **i**, it is pronounced like the **ch** in the Scottish word 'lo**ch**'. It doesn't exist in 'standard' English so some people opt for either a **k** or an **h** instead.
If the **g** comes before any other vowel, it is pronounced like the **g** in '**g**ood'.
Jorge, argentino, trabalenguas, largo, yogur, me gusta

h In Spanish this letter is silent.
hermano, hijo, habitación, hacer, helado, huevo

j This sound is pronounced as the **ch** in the Scottish word 'lo**ch**'.
garaje, hijo/a, naranja, jardín, oreja, ojo

ll This sounds very like the English y in yo-yo.
castillo, amarillo, mantequilla, cebolla, vainilla, bocadillo

ñ This should sound like **ny** in English, as in the name 'Ta**n**ya'.
España, año, cumpleaños, piña, señor, montaña

rr The double **r** should be rolled, like a purrrrring cat. This is a difficult sound for some English speakers but it's just a matter of practice!
perro, Inglaterra, marrón, pelirroja, arriba, mediterráneo

v Remember, in Spanish the letters **v** and **b** sound the same – like a softer version of the English **b**.
vivo, voy, verde, vacaciones, ventana, uva

z Like **c** after **e** or **i**, **z** is always pronounced as **th** in the English word '**th**in'.
diez, marzo, zanahoria, almuerzo, arroz, nariz

¡Salva el planeta!

9. Save the planet!

The Spanish and English languages are closely related through Latin so a lot of Spanish words are very like English words. Which of these are like English words?

Relaciona las palabras españolas con las palabras inglesas y subraya las que son similares.

Match the Spanish words with the English words and then underline the ones that are similar.

el planeta	climate
el sistema solar	the oceans
el medio ambiente	atmospheric pollution
la contaminación atmosférica	the solar system
los océanos	the satellite
los continentes	the environment
el clima	the planet
el satélite	the continents

Truco

Try to think of other words in English that resemble the last two in Spanish... (ambient, contamination). You can often guess what a word means because it looks like a synonym (a word that means the same) of its English translation.

Truco

The Spanish equivalent for 'honeymoon' is a direct translation: *luna de miel* ('moon of honey') so a *tierra de miel* is an 'earth of honey'.

Track 28

¡Chiste!

¿Qué hace la gente de la luna después de casarse?
What do moon people do after getting married?

¡Van a la tierra de miel!
They go on their honeyearth!

El sistema solar

The solar system

Mercurio es el planeta más cercano al **Sol**.
Venus se encuentra entre **Mercurio** y **la Tierra**.
Marte es el planeta más cercano a **la Tierra**.
Plutón es el planeta más alejado del **Sol**.
Neptuno es el planeta más cercano a **Plutón**.
Júpiter se encuentra entre **Marte** y **Saturno**.
Urano se encuentra entre **Saturno** y **Neptuno**.

Key words

el planeta planet
el Sol sun
la estrella star
la luna moon
la Tierra Earth
el satélite satellite
orbitar to orbit
cercano near
alejado far away
entre between
alrededor de around

¿Lo sabías?

Pluto is actually made up of two small planets, Pluto and Charon, so it is called 'a dwarf planet' *un planeta enano*.

Truco

Remember that *planeta* and *sistema* are both masculine words even though they end with *-a*.

Escribe los nombres de los planetas

Write the names of the planets

el Sol

1 2 3 4 5 6 7 8 9

1. .... 2. .... 3. ....

4. .... 5. .... 6. ....

7. .... 8. .... 9. ....

¿Cuál es el planeta más grande? ....

¿Cuál es el planeta más pequeño? ....

¡El medio ambiente está en peligro!

The environment is in danger!

Key words

la basura/los residuos rubbish
la contaminación pollution
el gas gas/fumes
el tubo de escape exhaust
la bolsa bag
el plástico plastic
la luz light

Casi 7 mil millones de personas viven en nuestro planeta.
Almost 7 billion people live on our planet.

Elige los títulos que corresponden a las imágenes

Choose the titles that go with the pictures

los gases del tubo de escape — car exhaust fumes
las bolsas de plástico — plastic bags
las luces — lights
la televisión — television
la contaminación — pollution
la basura — rubbish

1. ....
2. ....
3. ....

4. ....
5. ....
6. ....

Key words

reducir to reduce
utilizar to use
separar/clasificar to sort
apagar to switch off
desenchufar unplug

Escribe un eslogan para cada imagen

Write a slogan for each picture

"¡Separa la basura!"

....

....

¿Qué puedo hacer yo?
What can I do?

Puedes separar la basura: los envases de plástico y metal, el vidrio, el papel y el cartón.

You can sort your rubbish: plastic and metal containers, glass, paper and cardboard.

Elige el cubo correcto
Choose the right bin

Track 29

Key words
el bote tin; pot
la caja box
la lata can
la botella bottle
las sobras leftovers
el cubo bin
las peladuras peelings
el periódico newspaper

¿Lo sabías?
Do you know how much rubbish the average person produces every year?

373kg de restos
257kg de envase
38kg de diarios y cartón
35kg de vidrio
Total = **703kg**

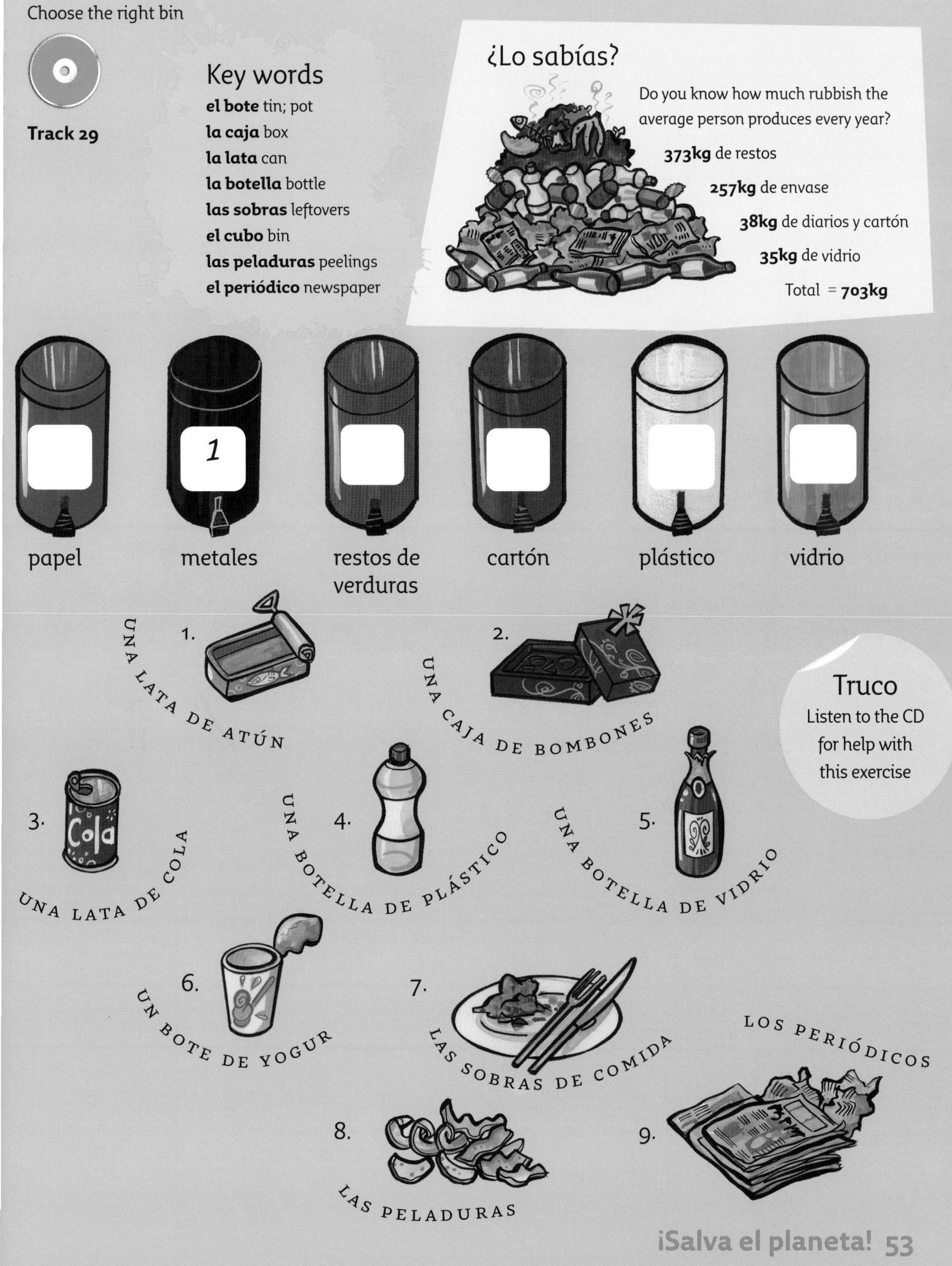

Truco
Listen to the CD for help with this exercise

¡Ahorra agua!

Save water!

¿Cuánta agua consumes al día?

How much water do you use a day?

Key words

el agua water
el litro litre
cada every
el día day
el mes month
el año year
consumir to consume

Cada día consumo .... litros de agua. Cada mes consumo .... litros de agua. Cada semana consumo .... litros de agua. Cada año consumo .... litros de agua.

Elige cinco maneras para proteger el medio ambiente y dibuja un cartel

Choose five ways of protecting the environment and draw a poster

ir
en autobús
en bici
a pie
en vez de en coche

poner
los residuos
las sobras
en el cubo

reciclar
el vidrio y las botellas
el cartón
el papel
las revistas y los diarios

respetar
la naturaleza: No coger flores silvestres

ahorrar
agua: Tomar una ducha en vez de un baño
electricidad: Apagar las luces

separar la basura

plantar un árbol

¡Salva el planeta!

Resumen

Summary

Subraya la excepción

Underline the odd one out

1. hermano	helado	madre	padre
2. rojo	pequeño	verde	azul
3. inglés	español	gracioso	argentino
4. enero	lunes	marzo	septiembre
5. Inglaterra	Escocia	Gales	España
6. Londres	Barcelona	Madrid	Valencia
7. Museo del Prado	Palacio Real	Sagrada Familia	Estadio Bernabéu
8. un perro	un pez	un gato	un hámster
9. una iglesia	una casa	un piso	un apartamento
10. la habitación	la cocina	el salón	el jardín
11. el queso	la carne	la leche	el jamón
12. el mar	el oeste	el sur	el este
13. deportista	hablador	guapo	febrero
14. música	bailar	jugar	comer
15. el pan	los cereales	el azúcar	el café
16. la cebolla	la patata	el pimiento	el plátano
17. el tren	el garaje	el bus	el coche
18. los ojos	las manos	los amigos	las orejas
19. Mercurio	la Tierra	el Sol	Marte
20. el papel	el vidrio	el cartón	la revista

Escribe "mi" o "mis"

Write *mi or mis*

1\. ... ... padre 2. .... padres 3. ... ... hermanas

4\. ... ... hermano 5. ... ... madre 6. ... ... abuelos

Escribe la palabra que falta

Write in the missing word

1. In Spanish all nouns are either .... or feminine.
2. The word for 'the' with masculine words is ....
3. The word for 'the' with .... words is la.
4. The word for 'the' with plural masculine words is ....
5. The word for 'the' with .... words is las.
6. Most nouns make the plural by adding .... or -es.

masculine el feminine los feminine -s

"Pequeño" o "pequeña"? Escribe la palabra correcta

Pequeño or pequeña? Write the correct word

1. Mi hermano es ....
2. Mi hermana es ....
3. Mi perro es ....
4. Mi casa es ....

pequeño
pequeño pequeña
pequeña

CD transcripts

Track 2

¿Quién es ese chico? ¿Cómo se llama?
Who is that boy? What's his name?
Se llama Lucas.
His name is Lucas.
¿De dónde es?
Where is he from?
Es de Argentina.
He's from Argentina.
¿Dónde vive?
Where does he live?
Vive en Buenos Aires.
He lives in Buenos Aires.
¿Cuántos años tiene?
How old is he?
Tiene once años.
He's eleven years old.
¿Tiene hermanos?
Does he have any brothers and sisters?
Sí, tiene un hermano y una hermana.
Yes, he has one brother and one sister.
¿Tiene un animal?
Does he have any pets?
Sí, tiene un gato.
Yes, he has a cat.
¿De qué color tiene el pelo?
What colour is his hair?
Tiene el pelo castaño.
He has brown hair.
¿Y sus ojos?
And his eyes?
Tiene los ojos verdes.
He has green eyes.
¿Cuál es su deporte favorito?
What is his favourite sport?
Es el fútbol.
It's football.
¡A mi también me gusta el fútbol! Bueno ¿jugamos al fútbol?
I like football too! Well, shall we play some football?

Track 3

¿Quién es?
Who is it?

Martina: Pues... ¿es una chica?
OK... is it a girl?
Ana: No.
No.
Martina: ¿Tiene el pelo corto?
Does he have short hair?
Ana: Sí.
Yes.
Martina: ¿Tiene los ojos marrones?
Does he have brown eyes?
Ana: No.
No.
Martina: ¿Tiene los ojos verdes?
Does he have green eyes?
Ana: Sí.
Yes.
Martina: ¿Lleva gafas?
Does he wear glasses?
Ana: Sí.
Yes.
Martina: ¡Es David!
It's David!
Ana: ¡Sí!
Yes!
Vale ¡ahora me toca a mí! ¿Es un chico?
OK, now it's my turn! Is it a boy?
Martina: No.
No.
Ana: Tiene media melena?
Does she have shoulder-length hair?
Martina: Sí.
Yes.
Ana: ¿Tiene el pelo negro?
Does she have black hair?
Martina: Sí.
Yes.
Ana: ¿Tiene los ojos azules?
Does she have blue eyes?
Martina: No, los tiene marrones.
No, she has brown eyes.
Ana: ¿Lleva sombrero?
Is she wearing a hat?
Martina: Sí.
Yes.
Ana: ¿Es Berta?
Is it Berta?
Martina: ¡Sí, muy bien!
Yes, well done!

Track 4

¿Cómo es Felipe?
What does Felipe look like?
Tiene el pelo corto, rizado y negro y los ojos marrones.
He has short curly black hair and brown eyes.
¿Cómo es Jorge?
What does Jorge look like?
Tiene el pelo corto y liso y los ojos marrones.
He has short, straight hair and brown eyes.
¿Isabel tiene los ojos azules?
Does Isabel have blue eyes?
Sí, y el pelo largo, ondulado y rubio.
Yes, and long, wavy, blond hair.
¿Cómo es Martina?
What does Martina look like?
Tiene los ojos verdes, y el pelo liso y media melena.
She has green eyes and straight, shoulder-length hair.
Lucas también tiene los ojos verdes, ¿no?
Lucas has green eyes too, doesn't he?
Sí, y tiene el pelo castaño y rizado. Y lleva gafas.
Yes, and he has brown, curly hair. And he wears glasses.
¡Ah sí! Ana tiene el pelo largo y negro y los ojos marrones.
Oh yes! Ana has long, black hair and brown eyes.
¡Sí, eso es!
Yes, that's right!

Track 9

Journalist: Ana, dibuja tu casa ideal. ¿Qué quieres tener en tu casa? ¿Un jardín grande?
Ana, draw your ideal house. What do you want to have in your house? A big garden?
Ana: Sí, en mi casa quiero un jardín grande con piscina.
Yes, in my house I want a big garden with a swimming pool.
Journalist: Un jardín grande... ¿Y una piscina?
A big garden... And a swimming pool?
Ana: Sí, una piscina con tobogán.
Yes, a swimming pool with a slide.
Journalist: ¿Con tobogán?
With a slide?
Ana: Sí. Y una mesa de ping-pong.
Yes. And a table tennis table.
Journalist: Y una mesa de ping-pong... ¿Y una pista de tenis?
And a table tennis table... And a tennis court?
Ana: No, no me gusta mucho el tenis.
No, I don't really like playing tennis.
Journalist: Vale. ¿Y un garaje?
Okay. And a garage?
Ana: Sí, un garaje.
Yes, a garage.
Journalist: ¿Con qué tipo de coche?
With what type of car?
Ana: Quiero tres coches: uno grande y dos pequeños.
I want three cars: one big and two small.
Journalist: ¿Y qué más?
And what else?
Ana: En el sótano un cine.
In the basement a cinema.
Journalist: ¿Un cine?
A cinema?
Ana: ¡Sí, un cine! ¡Me encanta ver películas!
Yes, a cinema! I love watching films!

Track 12

¿Dónde viven?
Where do they live?
¿Dónde vive Alberto?
Where does Alberto live?
Vive en Santander. Es una ciudad grande en el norte de España.
He lives in Santander. It is a big city in the north of Spain.
Una ciudad grande en el norte de España. Vale. ¿Y Marta?
A big city in the north of Spain. OK. And Marta?
Marta vive en un pueblo pequeño en el oeste de España.
Marta lives in a small town in the west of Spain.
Un pueblo pequeño en el oeste... ¿Y Ricardo?
A small town in the west... and Ricardo?
Ricardo vive en Valencia. Es una ciudad grande en el este, en la costa mediterránea.
Ricardo lives in Valencia. It's a big city in the east, on the Mediterranean coast.
Una ciudad grande en el este... ¿Y Sara?
A big city in the east... and Sara?
Ella vive en un pueblo grande en la Costa del Sol en el sur de España.
She lives in a big town on the Costa del Sol in the south of Spain.
Un pueblo grande en el sur... ¿Enrique, dónde vive?
A big town in the south. Enrique, where does he live?
Vive en un pueblo pequeño en las montañas, los Pirineos catalanes, en el norte.
He lives in a small town in the mountains, the Catalan Pyrenees, in the north.
¿Y Raquel? ¿Dónde vive?
And Raquel? Where does she live?
Vive en una ciudad pequeña en el centro del país.
She lives in a small city in the centre of the country.
Una ciudad pequeña en el centro de España... ¿Y José?
A small city in the centre of Spain... And José?
José vive en una ciudad pequeña en el este.
José lives in a small city in the east.
Una ciudad pequeña en el este. ¿Y Eva?
A small city in the east. And Eva?
Eva vive en un pueblo grande en Galicia.
Eva lives in a big town in Galicia.
¿Dónde?
Where?
En el oeste del país.
In the west of the country.
Muy bien. Gracias.
Very good. Thank you.

Track 13

Isabel: ¿Cómo es Rita?
What is Rita like?
Martina: Es habladora.
She's chatty.
Isabel: Rita es habladora. ¿Y Paco? ¿Cómo es?
Rita is chatty. And Paco? What is he like?
Martina: Paco... Paco es gracioso.
Paco... Paco is funny.
Isabel: ¿Ah, sí? ¿Y Mateo es gracioso también?
Really? And is Mateo funny too?
Martina: ¡Ay, no! Es deportista.
Oh no! He's sporty.

Isabel: Mateo es deportista... ¿Y Benito?
Mateo is sporty. And Benito?
Martina: ¿Benito? Es inteligente.
Benito? He's clever.
Isabel: Inteligente, ¿sí? ¿Y Miriam?
Clever, really? And Miriam?
Martina: Miriam es guapa.
Miriam is pretty.
Isabel: Sí, Miriam es guapa. ¿Y Alejandro?
Yes, Miriam is pretty. And Alejandro?
Martina: Alejandro es muy simpático.
Alejandro is very nice.
Isabel: ¿Y Claudio?
And Claudio?
Martina: Claudio es tímido.
Claudio is shy.
Isabel: ¿Ah, sí?
Really?
Martina: Sí, un poco.
Yes, a little.
Isabel: ¿Y Julia?
And Julia?
Martina: Julia es muy graciosa.
Julia is very funny.
Isabel: Sí, es graciosa. Y Jorge es guapo, ¿no?
Yes, she is funny. And Jorge is good-looking, right?
Martina: Sí, Jorge es guapísimo.
Yes, Jorge is very good-looking.
Isabel: ¿Y María?
And María?
Martina: María también es deportista. Le gusta el tenis.
María is sporty too. She likes tennis.
Teacher: ¡Isabel! ¡Martina! ¡Escuchad, por favor!
Isabel! Martina! Listen, please!
Isabel & Martina: Perdón, profesora...
Sorry, Miss.

Track 16

¿Qué hace Ana?
What is Ana doing?

Mamá: Ana ¿qué haces?
Ana, what are you doing?
Ana: Me despierto.
I'm waking up.
Mamá: ¿Qué haces?
What are you doing?
Ana: Me levanto.
I'm getting up.

Mamá: Ana ¡venga!
Ana, come on!
Ana: Sí, sí. Me lavo.
Yes, yes. I'm washing myself.

Ana: ¡Ay, mamá! ¿Dónde está mi jersey? Me visto.
Oh, mum! Where is my jersey? I'm getting dressed.
Mamá: Sobre tu cama.
On your bed.

Mamá: ¡Ana!
Ana!
Ana: ¡Voy, voy!
Coming, coming!

Ana: Pásame los cereales, por favor...
Pass me the cereal, please.
Mamá: ¿Los cereales? Toma.
The cereal? Here you are.
Ana: Gracias. Desayuno.
Thank you. I'm eating breakfast.

Mamá: Ana, son las siete y media.
Ana, it's half past seven.
Ana; Sí, me lavo los dientes.
Yes, I'm brushing my teeth.

Ana: Adiós, mamá. Salgo. Hasta luego.
Bye, mum! I'm leaving. See you later.
Mamá: ¡Adiós!
Bye!

Mamá: Ah, Ana. ¿Eres tú?
Oh, Ana. Is that you?
Ana: Sí, ya estoy en casa.
Yes, I'm home.

Mamá: ¿Qué haces, Ana?
What are you doing, Ana?
Ana: Estoy haciendo los deberes.
I'm doing my homework.

Mamá: Ana, son las nueve...
Ana, it's nine o'clock.
Ana: De acuerdo, mamá. Me acuesto.
Okay, mum. I'm going to bed.

Track 18

1. No como cereales. Como un yogur, una tostada con mermelada y bebo zumo de naranja.
   I don't eat cereal. I eat yoghurt, toast with marmalade, and I drink orange juice.
2. No como yogur. Como cereales con leche, pan con crema de chocolate, un plátano y bebo chocolate caliente.
   I don't eat yoghurt. I eat cereal with milk, bread with chocolate spread, a banana and I drink hot chocolate.
3. Como cereales con leche, una tostada con miel y bebo zumo de naranja. Mmmm, no. Bebo zumo de piña.
   I eat cereal with milk, toast with honey and I drink orange juice. Mmmm, no. I drink pineapple juice.
4. Como pan con aceite, jamón y queso y bebo café.
   I eat bread with oil, ham and cheese, and I drink coffee.

Track 19

Vendor: ¿Quieres un helado, Martina?
Would you like an ice cream, Martina?
Martina: Sí.
Yes.
Vendor: ¿Cuál?
Which?
Martina: Quiero un helado de frambuesa.
I'd like a strawberry ice cream.
Vendor: Isabel, ¿quieres un helado?
Isabel, would you like an ice cream?
Isabel: Sí, quiero un helado de vainilla.
Yes, I'd like a vanilla ice cream.
Vendor: ¿Y tu amiga, Ana?
And your friend, Ana?
Isabel: Ana quiere un helado de fresa.
Ana would like a strawberry ice cream.
Vendor: ¿Y Jorge, qué quiere?
And Jorge, what would he like?
Martina: Quiere un helado de pistacho.
He would like a pistachio ice cream.
Vendor: ¿Y Lucas?
And Lucas?
Martina: Prefiere un helado de coco.
He would prefer a coconut ice cream.
Vendor: ¿Y tú, Felipe?
And you, Felipe?
Felipe: ¿Yo? ¿Me toca a mí, por fin? Quiero un helado de chocolate, chocolate... chocolate... ¡Es delicioso!
Me? Is it my turn, finally? I'd like a chocolate ice cream, chocolate... chocolate... it's delicious!

Track 28

Martina: ¿Qué puedo hacer?
What can I do?
Jorge: Puedes reciclar los restos, los envases y los contenedores.
You can recycle your leftovers, your packaging and your containers.
Martina: ¿Dónde los pongo?
Where do I put them?
Isabel: En el cubo correcto. ¿Qué tienes?
In the correct bin. What do you have?
Martina: Tengo un bote de atún.
I have a tin of tuna.
Jorge: Ponlo en el cubo negro para metales.
Put it in the black bin for metals.
Martina: Metal... ¿Y una caja de bombones?
Metal... and a box of sweets?
Jorge: Papel... no. Rojo para el cartón.
Paper... no. Red for cardboard.
Martina: Cartón... ¿Y una lata de cola?
Cardboard... and a can of cola?
Isabel: Negro para metales.
Black for metals.
Martina: ¿Y una botella?
And a bottle?
Isabel: ¿De plástico?
Made of plastic?
Martina: Sí, de plástico.
Yes, of plastic.
Isabel: El cubo amarillo para el plástico.
The yellow bin for plastics.
Martina: ¿Una botella de vidrio?
A glass bottle?
Jorge: El cubo verde para el vidrio.
The green bin for glass.
Martina: ¿Un bote de yogur?
A yoghurt carton?
Jorge: El cubo amarillo para el plástico.
The yellow bin for plastics.
Martina: ¿Los restos?
Food leftovers?
Isabel: El cubo marrón para los restos vegetales.
The brown bin for food scraps.
Martina: ¿Las peladuras?
Some peelings?
Isabel: También el cubo marrón para los restos de verduras.
Also the brown bin for food scraps.
Martina: ¿Y los periódicos?
And newspapers?
Jorge: El cubo azul para el papel.
The blue bin for paper.
Isabel: ¿Eso es todo?
Is that everything?
Martina: Sí, es todo. ¡Terminado!
Yes, that's everything. Finished!
Isabel: Muy bien.
Great.

Y nosotros también, hemos terminado. ¡Adiós!
And we have finished too. Goodbye!

Extra vocabulary

Las nacionalidades

I am American	Soy americano/a
I am Australian	Soy australiano/a
I am British	Soy británico/a
I am Canadian	Soy canadiense
I am English	Soy inglés/inglesa
I am Irish	Soy irlandés/irlandesa
I am Scottish	Soy escocés/escocesa
I am Welsh	Soy galés/galesa

How to say what you are **not**:
I am **not** Spanish — No ***soy*** español(a)

Los números

0 cero	10 diez	20 veinte	30 treinta
1 uno	11 once	21 veintiuno	31 treinta y uno
2 dos	12 doce	22 veintidós	32 treinta y dos...
3 tres	13 trece	23 veintitrés	
4 cuatro	14 catorce	24 veinticuatro	40 cuarenta
5 cinco	15 quince	25 veinticinco	50 cincuenta
6 seis	16 dieciséis	26 veintiséis	60 sesenta
7 siete	17 diecisiete	27 veintisiete	70 setenta
8 ocho	18 dieciocho	28 veintiocho	80 ochenta
9 nueve	19 diecinueve	29 veintinueve	90 noventa

Verbs

When you look up a new verb up in the dictionary it will be in the infinitive
vivir (to live)
comer (to eat)

When you are talking about yourself you need to change the infinitive to the *yo* 'I' form of the verb. To make the *yo* form, just take off the last two letters and replace them with an *-o*:
vivo (I live)
como (I eat)

Remember that you don't usually need to say *yo* ('I'). The *-o* ending of the verb tells you who is speaking.

Spanish infinitives fall into three groups: Those that end in *-ar*, those that end in *-er*, and those that end in *-ir*.

Some of the most common verbs are irregular, which means that they don't follow the usual rules. Usually, when these verbs change from the infinitive the middle of the word changes a little. In the Top Ten Verbs list, these irregular verbs are marked with a *.

Top ten verbs

1. *soy I am
2. *estoy I am
3. *tengo I have
4. *voy I go
5. *hago I do
6. vivo I live
7. como I eat
8. bebo I drink
9. *juego I play
10. me gusta(n) I like

Los meses

enero January
febrero February
marzo March
abril April
mayo May
junio June
julio July
agosto August
septiembre September
octubre October
noviembre November
diciembre December

Los días de la semana

lunes Monday
martes Tuesday
miércoles Wednesday
jueves Thursday
viernes Friday
sábado Saturday
domingo Sunday

Las frutas

apple la manzana
banana el plátano
cherry la cereza
grape la uva
grapefruit el pomelo
lemon el limón
mango el mango
melon el melón
orange la naranja
peach el melocotón
pear la pera
pineapple la piña
plum la ciruela
raspberry la frambuesa
strawberry la fresa

Las verduras

aubergine la berenjena
bean el frijol
cabbage la col
carrot la zanahoria
cauliflower la coliflor
courgette el calabacín
cucumber el pepino
lettuce la lechuga
mushroom el champiñón
onion la cebolla
pea el guisante
pepper el pimiento
potato la patata
spinach la espinaca
tomato el tomate

Answer key

Pg 2
1. Martina
2. Marcos
3. Mariana
4. Coco

Pg 4
Se llama Lucas. Es argentino. Vive en Buenos Aires. Tiene once años. Tiene un hermano y una hermana. Tiene un gato. Tiene el pelo castaño. Tiene los ojos verdes. Su deporte favorito es el fútbol.

perro = dog
gato = cat
hámster = hamster
pececito rojo = goldfish
cobaya = guinea pig
conejo = rabbit

Pg 5
Se llama Isabel. Es canaria. Vive en Las Palmas. Tiene doce años. Su cumpleaños es el 24 de mayo. Tiene dos hermanas. Tiene un pececito rojo. Su deporte favorito es el tenis. Tiene el pelo rubio. Tiene los ojos azules.

Pg 6
1. Es Carlos.
2. Es Rosa.

Pg 7
1. Es David.
2. Es Berta.

1. Isabel
2. Felipe
3. Ana
4. Jorge
5. Martina
6. Lucas

Pg 8
1. Luisa
2. Daniel
3. Flora
4. Cristina
5. Antonio

Pg 9
Mi abuelo Alberto.
Mi abuela Flora.
Mi tía Elena.
Mi padre Francisco.
Mi madre Cristina.
Mi tío Antonio.
Mi primo Luís.
Mi hermano Daniel.
Yo.
Mi hermana Luisa.
Mi prima Laura.
mi padre
mis hermanas
mi madre
mis padres
mi hermano
mis hermanos

Pg 10
1. Felipe
2. Isabel
3. Martina
4. Jorge
5. Ana
6. Lucas

Pg 13
"Juan II es mi padre y Juana Enríquez es mi madre.
Mis abuelos se llaman Fernando I y Leonor Urraca.
Mi hermana se llama Juana.
Tengo cuatro hijas que se llaman Isabel, Juana, María y Catalina.
Mi hijo se llama Juan como yo." Fernando

Pg 14
una granja - un granjero
una casa - una familia
un castillo - un señor
un apartamento - un turista
una caseta de perro - un perro

Pg 15
Felipe's house has a red roof, a white balcony, the walls are yellow, the shutters are blue, and the door is green.

Pg 16
la habitación - bedroom
la cocina - kitchen
la entrada - entrance
la escalera - stairs
el jardín - garden
la sala de estar - sitting room
el comedor - dining room
el (cuarto de) baño - bathroom
el cuarto de juegos - playroom

Pg 17
1. el (cuarto de) baño
2. la sala de estar
3. el garaje
4. la habitación
5. la cocina
6. el cuarto de juegos

Pg 19
Ana wants: A big garden, a swimming pool, a slide, a table tennis table, a garage, and a cinema. No tennis court.

Pg 20
5 Spanish things: bull-fighting, the Sagrada Familia, the Alhambra, flamenco dancing, and paella.

Pg 22
El Palacio Real = 10
La Plaza Mayor = 7
El Parque del Buen Retiro = 4
La Puerta del Sol = 9
La Gran Vía = 2
La Catedral de la Almudena = 8
El Estadio Santiago Bernabéu = 3
La Plaza de España = 1
El Museo del Prado = 5
La Estación de Atocha = 6

Pg 23
1. El Palacio Real
2. La Plaza Mayor
3. El Parque del Buen Retiro
4. La Puerta del Sol
5. La Catedral de la Almudena
6. La Gran Vía
7. La Plaza de España
8. El Estadio Santiago Barnabéu
9. El Museo del Prado
10. La Estación de Atocha

Pg 24
Martina: Vivo en Granada.
Berta: Vivo en Jaca.
Juan: Vivo en Finisterre.
Pedro: Vivo en Valldemossa.
Ana: Vivo en Madrid.
Jorge: Vivo en Barcelona.

Pg 25
Alberto = big city, north
Marta = small town, west
Ricardo = big city, east
Sara = big town, south
Enrique = small town, north
Raquel = small city, centre
José = small city, east
Eva = big town, west

Pg 27
Martina: Soy más pequeña que Felipe
Felipe: Soy más grande que Martina
1. Elena
2. Cristina
3. Felipe

Pg 28
1. habladora
2. deportista
3. inteligente
4. guapa
5. graciosa
6. hablador

Pg 29
Rita = habladora
Paco = gracioso
Mateo = deportista
Benito = inteligente
Miriam = guapa
Alejandro = simpático
Claudio = tímido
Julia = graciosa
Jorge = guapo
María = deportista

Pg 31
Marta es tímida F
Juan es deportista V
Elena es inteligente V
Clara es guapa V
Leticia no es simpática F
Jorge es tímido F
Bernardo es hablador F

Pg 33
1. Me lavo
2. Desayuno
3. Me lavo los dientes
4. Cojo la mochila
5. Me levanto
6. Me pongo la chaqueta
7. Salgo
8. Me visto

1. It's three o'clock
2. It's midday
3. It's half past eight
4. It's five o'clock
5. It's quarter past nine
6. It's quarter to eleven
7. It's midnight

Pg 35
1. Se despierta
2. Se levanta
3. Se lava
4. Se viste
5. Desayuna
6. Se lava los dientes
7. Sale
8. Llega
9. Hace los deberes
10. Se acuesta

Pg 39
Pictures:
1. Ana
2. Martina
3. Felipe
4. Isabel

CD:
1. Ana
2. Felipe
3. Martina
4. Isabel

Pg 41
Ana = fresa (strawberry)
Felipe = chocolate (chocolate)
Martina = frambuesa (raspberry),
Jorge = pistacho (pistachio),
Isabel = vainilla (vanilla),
Lucas = coco (coconut)

Pg 44
Se levanta - 7 o'clock
Sale - 8:10
Las clases empiezan - 9 o'clock

Pg 45
el coche = car
el tren = train
la bicicleta = bicycle
el autobús = (public) bus
el autobús escolar = school bus
el pie = foot

Felipe = autobús escolar
Lucas = pie
Martina = tren
Isabel = autobús
Jorge = bicicleta
Ana = coche

Pg 47
1. Dura 105 minutos.
2. Dura 30 minutos.
3. Dura 45 minutos.
4. Dura 105 minutos.
5. Dura 105 minutos.
6. Dura 30 minutos.
7. Dura 30 minutos.
8. Duran 285 minutos. (4 horas y 45 minutos)
9. Duran 165 minutos. (2 horas y 45 minutos)
10. Dura 450 minutos. (7 horas y 30 minutos).

Pg 48
los ojos = para ver
las orejas = para oír
la nariz = para oler
la lengua = para saborear
las manos = para tocar

Tengo los ojos para verte,
Tengo las orejas para oírte,
Tengo la nariz para olerte,
Tengo las manos para tocarte,
Tengo brazos para abrazarte,
Y una voz para recitarte un poema.

Pg 50
el planeta = the planet
el sistema solar = the solar system
el medio ambiente = the environment
la contaminación atmosférica = atmospheric pollution
los océanos = the oceans
los continentes = the continents
el clima = climate
el satélite = satellite

Pg 51
1. Mercurio
2. Venus
3. la Tierra
4. Marte
5. Júpiter
6. Saturno
7. Urano
8. Neptuno
9. Plutón

¿Cuál es el planeta más grande? Júpiter
¿Cuál es el planeta más pequeño? Plutón

Pg 52
1. la basura
2. la televisión
3. las bolsas de plástico
4. la contaminación
5. las luces
6. los gases del tubo de escape

1. ¡Separa la basura!
2. ¡Desenchufa la televisión!
3. ¡Reduce la contaminación!
4. ¡Utiliza las bolsas de plástico!
5. ¡Apaga las luces!
6. ¡Reduce los gases del tubo de escape!

Pg 53
Papel: 9
Metales: 1, 3
Cartón: 2
Restos de verduras: 7, 8
Plástico: 4, 6
Vidrio: 5

Pg 56
1. hermano
2. pequeño
3. gracioso
4. lunes
5. España
6. Londres
7. La Sagrada Familia
8. un pez
9. una iglesia
10. el jardín
11. la leche
12. el mar
13. febrero
14. música
15. el café
16. el plátano
17. el garaje
18. los amigos
19. el Sol
20. la revista

Pg 57
1. mi
2. mis
3. mis
4. mi
5. mi
6. mis

1. masculine
2. el
3. feminine
4. los
5. feminine
6. -*s*

1. pequeño
2. pequeña
3. pequeño
4. pequeña